···· AND HE WILL BE YET WISER *Proverbs 9:9*

TEACH YOURSELF
TO FLY

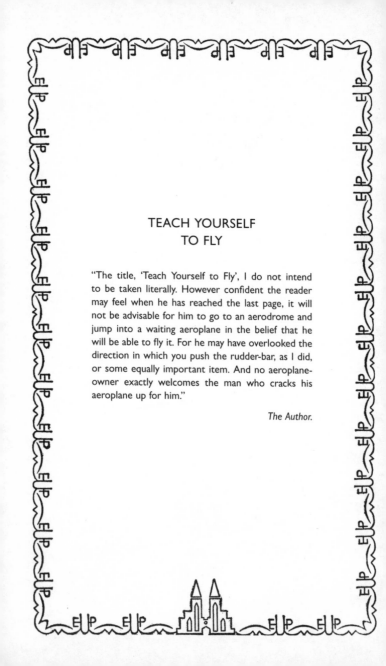

TEACH YOURSELF
TO FLY

"The title, 'Teach Yourself to Fly', I do not intend to be taken literally. However confident the reader may feel when he has reached the last page, it will not be advisable for him to go to an aerodrome and jump into a waiting aeroplane in the belief that he will be able to fly it. For he may have overlooked the direction in which you push the rudder-bar, as I did, or some equally important item. And no aeroplane-owner exactly welcomes the man who cracks his aeroplane up for him."

The Author.

TEACH YOURSELF TO FLY

By
SQUADRON LEADER
NIGEL TANGYE, R.A.F.O.

COMMEMORATIVE 1941 WARTIME EDITION

THE ENGLISH UNIVERSITIES PRESS
LONDON

First printed in September 1938. This facsimile is the fourth edition published in August 1941.

This edition first published in UK 2008 by Hodder Education, part of Hachette Livre UK, 338 Euston Road, London NW1 3BH.

This edition first published in US 2008 by The McGraw-Hill Companies, Inc.

The **teach yourself** name is a registered trademark of Hodder Headline.
Copyright © 1938 Nigel Tangye

British Library Cataloguing in Publication Data: a catalogue record for this title is available from the British Library.
Library of Congress Catalog Card Number: on file.

Printed in Great Britain for Hodder Education, an Hachette Livre UK Company, 338 Euston Road, London NW1 3BH, by Gutenberg Press Ltd, Malta.

Impression number   10 9 8 7 6 5 4 3 2
Year   2012 2011 2010 2009 2008

FOREWORD BY AIR CHIEF MARSHAL SIR GLENN TORPY, CHIEF OF THE AIR STAFF, ROYAL AIR FORCE

Seventy years ago, the prospect of a Second World War loomed ever larger. In 1938, deficiencies in British defence and the implications of Britain's military weakness for her strategic position had become apparent. By early October, the Services had been asked to report these deficiencies to the Cabinet and an ambitious rearmament programme began in earnest. The Supermarine Spitfire, which was to become an icon of the Battle of Britain, had just begun service with the Royal Air Force.

At the very same time, in September 1938, the first edition of Squadron Leader Nigel Tangye's *Teach Yourself to Fly* was published by Hodder and Stoughton Ltd. For aspiring aircrew, this legendary book often featured early in their career. Beautifully written, it captured the author's love of flying whilst explaining the concepts of flight in clear and entertaining prose. It comes as no surprise that the book was recommended by the Air Ministry to prospective Royal Air Force pilots as suitable for their study.

The 1941 edition, republished here to commemorate the 70th anniversary of the Teach Yourself series, contained a new chapter, 'Per Ardua ad Astra', which began with Churchill's quote: 'Never in the field of human conflict was so much owed by so many to so few'. With the Battle of Britain recently won, it was the most apt of introductions. The chapter described the various aircrew roles, all of which were reflected in the Royal Air Force's key commands: fighter, bomber and coastal. By the end of the War, the Royal Air Force's strength stood at over 1,200,000. Of these, nearly 200,000 were aircrew. The remainder, men and women, conscripts and volunteers, provided the essential support necessary to keep the aircraft flying, which eventually delivered victory. All in all, over 70,000 Royal Air Force personnel gave their lives in the course of the War.

I would like to congratulate Hodder Education on the 70th anniversary of the Teach Yourself series. I am delighted that they have chosen to mark the event with the republication of this wonderful book, especially as we also celebrate an important anniversary of our own in 2008 – the 90th anniversary of the Royal Air Force. Many congratulations and best wishes for the future.

SIR GLENN TORPY

FOREWORD TO THE FOURTH EDITION

WHEN this book was first published it had a happy compliment paid to it. It was recommended by the Air Ministry to prospective R.A.F. pilots as a suitable book for their study.

Since then we have passed from peace to war, but I have kept the flying instruction right up to date and the aircraft on which it is based is of the type extensively used in the Service for elementary instruction. However, I feel I should apologise for one or two unimportant references to civil flying facilities which are no longer available. They form a sentimental reminder of a world of long ago.

NIGEL TANGYE.

CONTENTS

LIST OF ILLUSTRATIONS

LIST OF ILLUSTRATIONS

INTRODUCTION

FOUR years before I had an opportunity to be flown in an aeroplane, I started to learn to fly. A few months later, when I had studied every text-book on the subject that I could find, I passed myself out in my mind as a fully qualified pilot. From then on, whenever I had a leisure moment, I would take flight in my mind with the most modern of aeroplanes. Sometimes I would soar into the still evening air in a single-seat fighter and have a glorious half-hour of aerobatics. Sometimes, when the weather was rough and forbidding, I would take my place as second pilot beside the commander of an air-liner on a regular air route, fighting the elements in order to maintain schedule. And sometimes I would take a rest from flying a land-plane and jump into a sea-plane, and change its element from blue water to blue sky by opening the throttle of its engines and coaxing it to rest on its wings, silver and shining in the sun. All this I did in my mind. All this I did with scrupulous attention to control movement, to engine temperatures and pressures, to wind strength and direction, to petrol con-

7

*

sumption—in fact, to everything that a pilot has to keep track of as he flies like a bird into the air and far into the sky. With the confidence of youth, I would have accepted the invitation of any pilot to take his machine into the air, so sure was I that my studies and my many flights in fancy had taught me all that was necessary for a pilot to know.

It was not until many years later that I had my first real lesson, and within a few minutes of being in the air I discovered, to my dismay, that, by some curious oversight at the very beginning of my self-instruction, I would have come to grief on my first flight in fancy; for I had mistaken the movement of the rudder bar. When I put my foot forward, the nose of the aircraft turned right instead of left.

But that mistake was soon rectified by my instructor, and I can truthfully say that, quite apart from the many happy hours of make-believe I had piloting an aeroplane, the study that I had made of flying halved the time of instruction that I would otherwise have needed before I was sent on my first solo. It is because of this experience, no less because of the enjoyment that lies in the study of flying by the enthusiast, that I have undertaken to write this book.

The title, " Teach Yourself to Fly ", I do not

intend to be taken literally. However confident the reader may feel when he has reached the last page, it will not be advisable for him to go to an aerodrome and jump into a waiting aeroplane in the belief that he will be able to fly it. For he may have overlooked the direction in which you push the rudder-bar, as I did, or some equally important item. And no aeroplane-owner exactly welcomes the man who cracks his aeroplane up for him.

Let him go to an aerodrome by all means, but let it be one with a flying-school, where the instructor will welcome him anyway, but will enthuse over him when he discovers that his pupil is familiar with all the controls, the flying jargon and the control movements of the more simple manœuvres in the air and on the ground. How much wearying, patient explaining will the instructor be spared! And how much, too, will the pocket of the pupil be spared!

I have not attempted in this book to touch on any evolution which could not be made in the simplest of planes. The machine I have had in my mind's eye has been an orthodox monoplane trainer fitted with an air-cooled engine of 130 horse-power, which gives it a speed around 100 miles an hour. The two seats are arranged in tandem—that is, one behind the other—with the instructor sitting in the front one. A simple system of voice-tubes and earphones enables the occupants to talk to one another. If I introduced machines that were equipped with the various appendages and devices, such as variable-pitch propellers, constant-pitch propellers, flaps, retractable under-carriages and tricycle under-carriages, the lessons would become too complicated for a clear picture of flying to remain in the mind of the pupil reader. All these devices have appeared in the last few years, and so complicated have aeroplanes other than training machines become, that even ex-perienced pilots have to study the instrument dashboard and controls for half an hour or so before they feel ready to take the machine up for the first time. Almost gone are those happy, carefree days when a new type of aeroplane would appear out of the sky and land on the aerodrome, and the owner would come over to you and say, " Like to try her ? " There are, alas ! too many gadgets about an aeroplane now for an owner to feel so confidently generous.

Another point about this book I should explain is the sequence of instruction I have followed. When you actually learn to fly, you will, for instance, be taught to fly straight and level before you learn to take off. In this book, for interest's sake, I have gone straight through the sequence of events that face a pilot from the time

he gets into his aeroplane to the time he jumps out
of the cockpit after his flight.

You will gain considerable assistance for your
study of this book if you take a passenger flight
in an aeroplane before you start reading it.   This
experience will make everything easier for you to
appreciate, because you will be able to have a
realistic background in your mind of what it feels
like to fly and what the earth looks like far below you; and you will have the satisfaction of
learning that when you are in an aeroplane there
is no sensation of giddiness, as when you are
looking over the parapet of a high building.   You
view the earth, which lies perhaps thousands of
feet below you, with a feeling of complete detach-
ment and, unless you are a very nervous type, of
sure security—so long as you have not chosen as
your pilot a friend who thinks it a good opportunity to " show off ".   More people have been
put off flying by choosing wrongly the circumstances of their first flight than by any other cause.
An experienced pilot knows that when he is taking
up a passenger on his first flight, the novelty of
flying is quite enough to make him appreciatively
impressed by the pilot's capabilities.   He does not
wish to be thrown about the sky, as is so often
done by the young and arrogant pilot who is
taking a friend up for the first time.   If he does

throw his plane about under these circumstances, you may be pretty sure he is doing it badly into the bargain, so that you are doubly advised to keep clear of him. A fine pilot just simply will not do it, unless you specifically ask him to aerobat—in which case he will do some of the more gentle evolutions, and be ready to stop the instant he sees you begin to look a bit green.

No, on principle, keep clear of your friends for your introduction to the air. When you know something about flying you will be able to judge their ability for yourself. You can then make whatever use you can of them, provided they satisfy you that they are safe !

A joy-ride flight is not so out of reach as is often thought. There are more than a hundred aerodromes up and down the country which keep aircraft in which short or long passenger flights are given, and the cost is from as little as five shillings for a five-minute trip up to anything you like to pay.

Take the earliest opportunity, therefore, to find out which is your nearest aerodrome where joy-rides are given, and then go and have your baptism of the air. It will be a glorious experience and one which you will never forget.

When your pilot has helped you into your cockpit and climbs into his own, you will inevitably feel a little tense. The machine, to your un-practised eye, will appear to be a frail craft in which to entrust your life by taking you up into the air at a hundred miles an hour. Remember that an aeroplane is the strongest machine for its weight that has ever been built by Man, and take comfort accordingly. *Relax.* Loosen your muscles and sit quite calmly in your seat. And *Relax.* That is the secret of enjoying flying from the first moment that you sit in an aeroplane. The pilot will taxi the machine out into the best position on the aerodrome, for the take-off, which always has to be made into wind. As it trundles over the uneven ground, you will be bounced about a bit, though that is an exaggeration. Do not worry. As soon as your pilot opens his throttle and the plane starts to get air-borne, this juddering will diminish, until, when the wheels have kissed the grass a brief farewell, it will have stopped altogether, and you are floating smoothly on an invisible sea, the earth speeding beneath your wing-tips and miraculously fading farther and farther away. On certain days, either when it is very hot weather or windy, the air will be a little bumpy. You will feel the plane rising and dropping in small, sudden movements. If this happens, your instinct will play you false and your muscles will tauten. Again you must apply the golden rule and *relax*. You will then find the bumps are not at all frightening.

Incidentally, your instinct will often play you false when flying. Treat it as a fickle jade, and you will do much better. Instinct often tells you to go slow in the air—when flying near the ground in fog, for instance—but you must fly fast : as fast as you can, so that you have all the control necessary to clear a sudden obstacle. When you are flying in cloud by instruments, your instinct will often all but persuade you that your instrument is lying. The needle shows you to be flying straight, but your instinct shouts in your ear, louder and louder, that you are turning to the left. Be strong, and pay no attention to its voice. Your instrument will be right. And when you have been flying on a compass course for some time over country on which you have been unable to pick out a landmark, the voice of your instinct will start whispering in your ear that your compass is wrong. It will soon be shouting in your ear that the compass is leading you too far to the right. No wonder you cannot pick up the expected land-mark. But pay no attention to your instinct on such an occasion. Trust your compass.

When you get into the air, take a good look round you, and try to imprint in your memory what you see and what you feel, so that when you get down you have more than just an "amuse-ment-park" experience to remember. Look at the ground beneath you, and see what landmarks stand out most. Notice how clear is the pattern of roadways, and how marked is the tenuous line of the railway. See how woods form well-defined shapes, likewise lakes or reservoirs. These are the sort of landmarks which the pilot uses to find his way, by fitting their pattern on his map to the life-size pattern on the ground.

You will not be in the air long before your pilot does a turn. Unless you know what is happen-ing, this is apt to be rather an alarming experience. If he turns to the left, your left wing will dip and your right wing rise, until the whole aeroplane is tilted to the left and it starts to turn. Now is the moment to relax again. Do not obey the instinct which will influence you to lean outwards from the turn. Treat it for what it is—a fickle jade—and pay no attention, but relax and sit quite naturally in the seat. However far the pilot tilts the plane, you will find that there is no tendency for you to fall out.

Try to persuade the pilot, before you go up, to fly above the clouds, for this is an experience you will never forget. Maybe on the day you choose for your first flight there will be no clouds, or perhaps they will be too high for the pilot to reach.

But ask him to take you to them if it is humanly possible. The inside of a cloud is no different from a thick fog. The wings of your plane stretch into it on either side of you, their tips nearly obscured, and you feel as though you are quite still. Only the roar of the engine and the needle of the air-speed indicator will tell you that you are flying at nearly 100 miles an hour. As the aeroplane climbs up through it, the bleak unfriend-liness of the fog becomes brighter, until, just before the plane breaks through the top, the white glare around you strains your eyes. Then all of a sudden you are clear of it, and you find yourself in a dazzling firmament of sunshine, an unbroken surface of glistening snow beneath you and a limitless bowl of blue sky above. Cut off from the world of reality, you are suspended alone in a world of fantasy which the most virile imagination could not picture to its full extent. And perhaps as impressive as anything is the perfect smooth-ness of the air in which you fly, for there are rarely air currents to disturb the serenity of even flight above the clouds.

The return through the clouds is as depressing as the climb is exhilarating. The eye has become accustomed to the vital splendour of the sun and sky, with the result that the air-space between cloud and earth appears to be gloom personified.

But after a few minutes the eye once more attunes itself to the sunless light, and the gloom disappears.

You may have a slight shock, on this first flight of yours, when the even note of the engine suddenly stops and there is silence, except for the swish of wind over wing and fuselage. Be prepared for this and it will not disturb you. It is only the pilot throttling down his engine to start his glide down onto the aerodrome. In order to lose height, he does not need his engine—rather in the same way when you are coasting down a hill in a car, the force of gravity is quite sufficient to keep you going. It is only when the attitude of the vehicle is such that it is fighting gravity that you need power to combat it. Try to pick out the aerodrome as early as possible, so that you can follow the pilot's movement of the plane as he judges his approach to it. It is this part of flying, and the judgment required in landing gently at 50 miles an hour or so, that you will find most difficult to surmount when you are learning.

Throughout this approach, remember the golden rule—I cannot repeat it too often—relax. You may think, as you get near the ground and begin to see the speed at which you are travelling, that he is sure to hit that hedge which bounds the aerodrome. Have no fear. He will clear it all right. Nor is he going to hit the ground with the bump that you expect as the ground rushes a few feet beneath you. You will hardly feel the moment of contact of wheels and ground. Only the juddering of the under-carriage and the change of attitude of the machine as the tail comes down and rests on the ground will tell you that you are on earth again.

After the pilot has taxied his machine back to the hangars, wait for him to get out before you do so. He will tell you where to put your feet, because damage can be done to the plane if you make a false step. Ask him all the questions you like, and then you will be equipped to read this book to full advantage.

CHAPTER I

CONTROLS AND INSTRUMENTS

BEFORE you go in the air on your first lesson, it will be necessary for you to have the various vital parts of the aeroplane explained to you. Exercise a little patience, and bear with me while I give you some definitions which are necessary for me to use in the ensuing pages if I can hope to meet with success in translating the movement and sense of flying onto paper.

You have arrived at the aerodrome, met your instructor and committed yourself to a course of flying. The aeroplane in which you are going to be given your lessons is resting on the tarmac in front of the hangar. It is a low-wing mono-plane—that is, an aeroplane with a single wing on which rests the fuselage, so that the floor of the cockpit is roughly on a level with the top surface of the wing. One cockpit, in which will sit your instructor, is immediately behind the engine; the other cockpit is a couple of feet behind the front one, and so placed that when you sit in it you can see over the side directly beneath you, because it is placed just behind the wing.

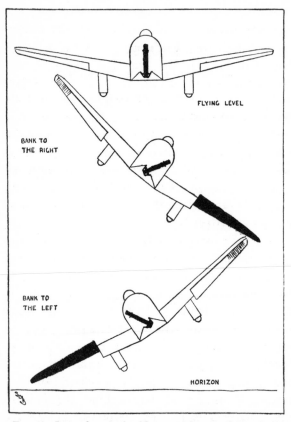

FIG. 1.—Lateral control. Note position of stick and ailerons in relation to the attitude of the machine. The amount of aileron movement is exaggerated for the sake of clarity.

When you come near to the plane, you will see details which need explaining. Stretching from half-way along the rear edge, called the *trailing edge*, of each wing to the tips, is a flap which is hinged to the *rear spar* (inside the wing, so that you cannot see it) of the wing. These two flaps are *ailerons*, and are vital control surfaces. If you lift the right-wing aileron and look over the fuselage to the one on the other wing, you will see that the left-wing aileron goes down; and if you depress the right-wing aileron you will see that the left-wing aileron goes up. This is because they are interconnected at the Joystick, or *control column*, in the cockpit. Now walk over to the cockpit and move the control column (often called by pilots the *stick*) to the left and right, and at the same time watch the ailerons. By moving the stick to the left, you will see the left-hand aileron hinge upward and the right-hand aileron hinge downward. Move the stick to the right, and the reverse happens.

This aileron control is the way a pilot *banks*, or tilts, his aeroplane from one side to the other, and it happens in this way. Suppose he is flying along at 100 miles an hour, and he wishes to lower his left wing; he moves his stick over to the left, which hinges the left aileron upward. The rush of air over the left wing strikes this aileron, and naturally tries to blow it out of its way. What happens? The aileron is pushed downwards, but because the pilot is holding on to the stick and the aileron is attached to the wing, the wing-tip is pushed downwards. The same thing happens to the other wing in the reverse direction, because the right aileron is depressed and the rushing air pushes the right wing-tip up. The whole aeroplane therefore turns around its *longitudinal axis* (an imaginary line drawn through the *fuselage*, or body, from nose to tail) until the pilot centralises the stick and the ailerons return to their original position flush with the wing. The movement of the plane around its longitudinal axis is helped by the ailerons in another way. Without going into aerodynamical details, the lift of a wing is increased a little by an aileron being depressed and decreased by an aileron being raised. Because of this fact, a wing which is dipped, due to the resistance of its raised aileron to the air-stream, is helped further to dip by the loss of lift to that wing. At the same time, the gain in lift of the opposite wing helps the plane to rotate about its longitudinal axis.

One cannot leave the subject of ailerons without mentioning aileron drag. It is quite simple to follow, but should be understood thoroughly if accurate flying is the aim of the pilot. Suppose he puts his stick over to the right in order to bank to the right; the right-wing aileron comes up and the left-wing aileron goes down. The position of these ailerons relative to the wing is such that the depressed aileron (the one on the left wing in this case) offers more resistance to the air than the raised aileron. There is therefore a force exerted which tends to pull (drag) back on the left wing-tip, with the result that the nose of the plane relative to the tail is pulled to the left a little as soon as the pilot puts his stick over to the right. The same thing happens in the opposite direction when he puts his stick over to the left in order to bank left. This movement of the nose is called *yaw*.

The control surface which deals with yaw more than any other is the *rudder*. Take a good look at it. You will see that you can move it from side to side in the same way as you can move the ailerons. But instead of being hinged on a horizontal spar, it is hinged on the vertical *fin*, which is fixed to the fuselage in the centre of the tailplane. You will see that the rudder has about a 30-degree movement on either side of the centre line of the fuselage. Now go to the cockpit and climb into it. Where you put your feet you will find a horizontal bar. This bar is pivoted about a pin at its centre, and is connected by wires to the rudder in such a way that when you push your left foot forward the rudder is deflected to the left.   When in the air, the air-stream striking this deflected rudder surface tries to push it out of its way, with the result that the tail of the aeroplane is pushed round and the nose of the plane yaws to the left.   Put in its simplest terms, if you want the nose to turn to the left, you push your left

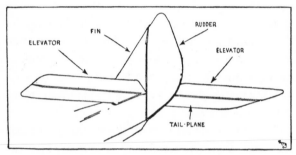

FIG. 2.—Normal tail unit seen from below and behind.

foot forward, and to the right your right foot forward. *The movement of the pivoted " steering " bar is therefore just the opposite to the movement of a bicycle handle-bar.*

Before you leave the rudder for the time being, take a look at the fin.   At first sight this appears to be in line with the centre line of the fuselage, and it serves the obvious function of helping to keep the machine straight.   But if you look closely, you will see that it is just a few degrees out of the centre line. This is because the revolving propeller pushes the air back (it is the reaction to this which pulls the aeroplane forward) in a corkscrew shape, sweeping it back over the fuselage in a spiral. If the fin was built in line with the fuselage, the air-stream would strike it at a slight angle all the time, with the result that, far from the fin helping the pilot to keep the machine straight, it would be tending to turn it. To counter this spiral effect, the fin is therefore set at the slight angle to the centre line of the fuselage which you can observe.

You have now been shown the rudder control, which controls yaw, and the aileron controls, which control the banking of the plane around the longitudinal axis. There is one more control to see, and that is the elevator, which is hinged to the trailing edge of the tailplane on either side of the rudder. This control surface is hinged horizontally, and can therefore be moved up and down. Applying exactly the same principle to it as the action of the air-stream on rudder and ailerons, it is easy to understand that when the elevator is raised, the tail of the aeroplane is pushed down by the air-stream, with the result that the aeroplane assumes an attitude in which the nose is higher than when in normal flight. The elevator is attached to the stick in such a manner that when the pilot wishes to climb, he eases the stick back, and when he wants to dive, he eases it forward.

In all these control movements it is very important to realise that they work only so long as the stick is out of its central position. As soon as the pilot has attained the attitude he desires, then he centralises his stick and the aeroplane will maintain that attitude. There are exceptions to this which will be explained later, but in principle that is what happens.

While you are looking at the tail unit (Fig. 2), a refinement must be explained to you. It is easy to understand that under various conditions of load an aeroplane will be out of balance. In other words, it will not tend, without constant attention by the pilot, to fly level as it should do. This may happen when a heavy pilot has been flying the aeroplane in perfect trim and the next man to take it up is light in weight. Under such conditions it is reasonable to understand that the aeroplane is out of trim for the lightweight pilot. The nose of the machine will either tend to drop or rise, according to the change of position of the centre of gravity of the machine occasioned by the different weight of the two pilots. Suppose the nose tended to drop—in other words, the machine was *nose heavy* (the opposite inclination is *tail heavy*)—the pilot would have to exert pressure on the stick in order to keep the elevators in the " up " position all the time he required to fly level. This is very undesirable. In your training aircraft you will see a lever which works in a quadrant attached to the side of the cockpit. This is called the *tail trim* (Fig. 5) and, according to the position it is set in the quadrant, it increases or decreases tension in a spring attached to the foot of the stick. The pilot can therefore set it to the position which allows all pressure necessary on the stick to keep the aeroplane flying level to be taken up by the spring. In larger aeroplanes trim is obtained by a similar control, but instead of there being a spring acting on the stick, there is a wheel which is connected to the tailplane. Movement of the wheel by the pilot either lowers or raises the front edge (the *leading edge*) of the tail-plane so that its attitude in relation to the air-stream is altered. According to the amount the tail-plane is moved, so the pressure by the pilot on the stick is relieved.

A moment's thought, and you will see that the three controls that I have just explained allow a pilot complete freedom of movement in the air. Various combinations of all three enable him to put his machine in whatever attitude he likes.

When you have got this quite clear in your mind (I should cut out a paper model, if I were you, and see it that way, if you cannot quite grasp it), go back to the cockpit and have a look at the instrument-board (Fig. 3).   In a training aeroplane this is quite a simple affair, and very different from the

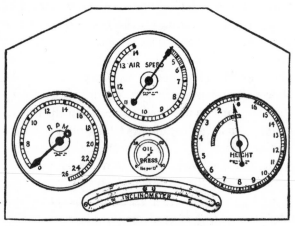

FIG. 3.—The essential instruments.

immensely complicated dashboard of a military plane or an air-liner.   With the latter type of plane, a pilot *has* to watch certain of his instruments if he is to take off, fly and land in safety. But with a light plane, like the one in which you are going to learn to fly, instruments are a help to the pilot, but not essential to him.

Outstanding among the dials which you see on

the dashboard (*instrument panel*) is one with
A.S.I. written on its face and a series of figures
from 4 to 14 on its circumference. A needle is
pointing to the figure 4. This is the air-speed
indicator, and obviously, as its name implies, it
tells you your air speed : the figure 4 stands for
40 miles an hour, the 5 for 50, the 10 for 100, and

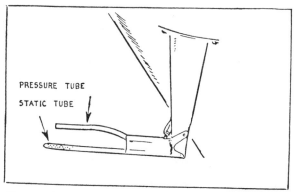

PRESSURE TUBE

STATIC TUBE

FIG. 4.—Pitot head through which the air speed is indicated,
by air pressure, on the A.S.I.

so on. It starts at 40 because the *stalling speed*
of the aeroplane, which is the critical speed below
which the aeroplane will not fly because it has
not generated enough air pressure around the
wings to keep it *air-borne*, is about 45 miles an
hour. This critical speed varies with each type of
aeroplane and, generally speaking, gets higher the
faster the machine. It is always the aim of

designers to get as high a top speed and as low a stalling speed as possible, which is naturally the landing speed, too. The A.S.I. (sometimes called the *pitot*, pronounced peeto) is worked by air pressure formed by the speed of the machine. If you look below the wing (sometimes it is put in front of the wing), you will see a curious contraption which looks like two pencils jutting out forward (Fig. 4). Never mind what one of these is there for, but the other is open at its front end. It is connected by tube to a diaphragm in the A.S.I. itself, and according to the pressure of air this diaphragm is pushed out or in. Attached to it is the needle which you see, and it is a simple matter to calibrate the face of the instrument in miles per hour instead of air-pressure, because the two are inter-related. You can therefore understand that the A.S.I. does not tell the pilot what speed he is flying at *over the ground*, but only *in the air*. He can only tell what speed he is flying at over the ground by knowing the speed and direction of the wind at whatever height he is flying. Suppose the A.S.I. tells him that his speed is 100 miles an hour; if he is flying against a 10-mile-an-hour wind, his speed over the ground will be only 90 miles an hour; if he is flying with the wind, his speed over the ground will be 110 miles an hour. If he is flying across wind, then his *ground speed* is a compromise. So remember that the A.S.I. only gives him his *air speed*.

Another dial, similar to the A.S.I., with calibrations around its circumference and a needle, is the *altimeter*. This instrument, like the A.S.I., is limited in the information it gives to the pilot. It works exactly like a barometer, according to atmospheric pressure. The higher you fly, the lower becomes the atmospheric pressure. At ground-level this is about 15 lb. per square inch, but at 15,000 feet this has been reduced by one half. Instead of the face being calibrated in pounds per square inch, it is marked in thousands of feet, because the two are inter-related, as I have already explained. Because of the fact that the atmospheric pressure varies from day to day, there is a simple device on the altimeter to enable the pilot to set it at 0 before he takes off. But it is most important to remember that the altimeter only tells him his height above his starting-point and *not* his height above the particular place he may be flying at any one time. If the height of his starting-point is known, he can get a little more accuracy by setting the needle to the height instead of to the 0, in which case he will know at any time during his flight his height above sea-level. If you can invent an instrument which will tell a pilot his height above the ground over

B

which he is flying at any time, your fortune is made. It is one of the most important things which is lacking in aviation. At present a pilot flying in fog has only a rough idea how high he is above the ground, with the result that he sometimes miscalculates his position and crashes into a hillside which he did not know was there.

The third dial, which is roughly the same size as the A.S.I. and the altimeter, is the engine revolution counter (*rev counter*). There is little to say about this instrument, as its name is self-explanatory. It tells the pilot what speed his engine is *revving* at, and also if it is running smoothly. If there is vibration at all, the needle will be shivering all the time. The pilot alters the engine revs by moving the *throttle*, which is the lever you see fixed at hand-level on the left-hand side of the cockpit. This lever stays in whatever position it is put.

The *oil-pressure gauge* is a small dial which, as its name implies, keeps the pilot informed of the oil pressure of the engine. This is a most important instrument, as a slackening in the normal oil pressure is often the first evidence of there being something wrong. If the pilot fails to keep an eye on his oil pressure, the value of that warning is lost to him, and the first thing he knows is that his engine has stopped. This fortunately occurs

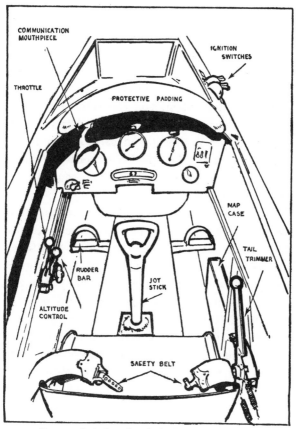

FIG. 5.—Interior of cockpit showing controls, dashboard and other fittings.

very rarely nowadays, but in flying, above everything else, to be forewarned is to be forearmed.

But for a clock, which is an essential part of
aerial navigation, there are no other dials on the
dashboard. But the clock is an important
instrument. If you know your speed and you
know the time taken, you can tell the distance
you have flown in a given period. Alternatively,
if you know the time taken to fly between two
landmarks and the distance between them,
measured from your map, then you can estimate
your ground speed.

Somewhere within the pilot's reach are two
switches. These are the engine-switches. I know
there is only one engine, but there are two switches,
all the same. This is because all aero-engines
(except a few of the ultra-light engines) have two
ignition systems, as a safety precaution. The
magneto is one of the most delicate parts of a
petrol engine, and therefore one of the most likely
to go wrong. If an engine has two of them, and
one goes wrong, the other will take you home all
right. That is the reason for having a dual system.
Now, then, take a good look at the position of
those switches. They are pointing downwards,
and the engine, of course, is off. Remember you
are examining this machine with me as it lies on
the tarmac in front of the hangar. Their position

surprises you, does it not? When you turn an electric light in your house *on*, you push the switches *down*. When you switch it *off*, then you push the switches *up*. With an aero-engine, you do just the reverse. To switch it *off*, you push *down* the switches; to switch it *on*, you push them up. Get that well into your head, because it is very important, and nasty accidents have happened when novices have forgotten, and mechanics have been badly injured swinging propellers of engines which they have been told by novice pilots were switched off, when all the while they have been on.

At the top of the dashboard there is an instrument which looks like a slightly curved spirit-level with a bubble at its centre. This is the inclinometer, and is valuable in helping a pilot to fly accurately, especially to make accurate turns. Its function will be explained in more detail in the chapter on turning.

Everybody can recognise a compass when he sees one. In the aeroplane cockpit it may be on the dashboard in a vertical position, or it may be on a special little ledge in a horizontal position. At all events, you need not worry about that now. You have a lot to learn before you will need a compass.

Before you leave your examination of the

aeroplane, take a look in the front cockpit in
which your instructor will sit. You will see he
has a stick, too, and a rudder bar, and some
instruments. And if you move his stick and look
into the rear cockpit at the same time, you will
see that the stick there moves as though you were
guiding it yourself. In fact, you are. All the
controls—stick, rudder-bar, throttle and tail-
trim—in each cockpit are connected. This is
called *dual control*, and enables an instructor to
take over from you at an instant's notice, if need
be, and also to show you every movement before
you try it yourself. He can speak to you, too, by
the *voice-tube* installation. In each cockpit there
is a mouthpiece at the end of a flexible tube which
leads into the other cockpit. The other end is
left open. Over this you attach, when you sit
in the cockpit, the open end of the tube which
connects your headphones in your helmet. In
this connection, remember it is of the utmost
importance to your instruction for you to *hear*
everything. Go to some pains, therefore, when
ordering your flying-helmet, to see that the hole
of the earphones fits exactly over the cavity in
your ear. To get this right you may have to
have a helmet specially made for you. Never
mind. Get it made. The few extra shillings will
come out very much cheaper in the long run than

prolonged flying lessons due to your not being able to hear properly. Besides, it is infuriating for a flying instructor to be handicapped in his teaching because of his pupil's inability to hear his instructions properly.

You have now been introduced to the essential parts of the aeroplane in which you are going to learn to fly. You are ready for your first lesson. But before you walk away to the clubhouse to put on your flying clothing, take a look at the wheels. In front of each is a *chock*—a block of inclined wood to which is attached a length of rope. The purpose of these is so that the engine can be started without the aeroplane moving forward. When all is ready, the pilot waves to the mechanic, and he pulls them away, leaving the wheels free to revolve.

CHAPTER II

TAXYING

You may think that taxying an aeroplane (moving it under its own power on the ground) is an easy thing to do. It is, in fact, a difficult thing to do, and one which requires much practice if quite serious accidents are to be avoided.

When you get in your cockpit for your first lesson, there will be nothing for you to worry about. The instructor will show you how to fix your helmet and earphones and how to strap yourself in. Listen to him when he tells you always to strap yourself in. It is not so much the possibility of falling out that a belt is designed to prevent, but to save you as much as possible if, for some unfortunate reason, you have a crash. It will take up the shock which otherwise your head would have taken on the dashboard. Accidents are most likely to happen near the ground. It is for this reason that in all American air-liners a notice is flashed in the cabin when the pilot is about to take off or land. It reads, " Fasten Safety-Belts ". When you are high in the air and you are not going to do aerobatics, then there is no reason why you should not undo the belt. But always have it fastened before taking off or landing, or when you are flying low.

That is somewhat of a digression, but it is very important. As soon as the instructor has fixed himself up in his cockpit, he will be ready to start the engine. He turns on the petrol and shouts to the mechanic who is standing by the propeller :

" Switches off. Suck in."

At this order, the mechanic starts pulling over the propeller in its direction of rotation and, if you look at your throttle lever, you will see that the instructor has moved it forward. This is to fill the cylinders with petrol mixture in order to facilitate starting. When the mechanic has made half a dozen turns, he will stop and wait for your instructor to shout :

" Contact ! "

As soon as the instructor has pulled the throttle lever back and moved the engine's switches to the " on " position (switches pointing up) he will shout " Contact ", the mechanic will swing down on the propeller and the engine will burst into life, the instructor nursing it by moving the throttle slightly backwards and forwards until the engine settles down at a steady speed.

From now on, I am going to be your instructor sitting in the front seat and in communication with you by voice-tube. So let me impress upon you two things which you must remember if you are going to learn to fly in the minimum of time. First, *do what you are told, and only what you are told ;* and secondly, *if you do not understand anything, ask for it to be explained.* This is most important. I remember a pupil of mine wasting hours of time and pounds of his money because he did not understand the first principle of landing when I first explained it to him, although he said he understood fully at the time. It was not until we had been doing a dozen lessons and getting nowhere that I discovered that he was ignorant of this first principle which he had assured me he had followed when I started his lessons on landing.

As soon as the engine has started, put the throttle in such a position that the rev counter shows the engine to be doing about 800 revs a minute. Keep the engine running at this speed for at least four minutes, so as to enable the oil to get thoroughly warmed up and to penetrate between every moving surface of the engine. At the end of this time push the throttle slowly forward. The engine speed will immediately accelerate, until, when the throttle will not go any farther (when it is at *full throttle*), the rev counter is showing about 1800 revs or whatever the engine should rev at on the ground. This is different for different engines and different propellers. If it revs at anything below a hundred revs short of the proper maximum, switch off and tell the mechanic. There must be something wrong. While you are *revving up* the engine like this, hold the stick as far back as it will go into your stomach. This will keep the elevator on the tail up, and the slip-stream from the propeller striking its inclined surface, will keep the tail of the aeroplane firmly on the ground. As soon as you are satisfied that the engine is giving the proper amount of revs, ease back the throttle to the half-way position. Now, then, while looking at the rev counter, switch off one magneto circuit and then the other. This is to test each circuit. There should not be more than a drop of 50 revs when you do this. As soon as you are satisfied that all is well as a result of these tests, and that the engine is running smoothly, ease back the throttle so that the engine is just *ticking over*, and wave to the mechanic to take away the chocks. You are now free to taxi out onto the aerodrome.

The two main things to remember while taxying are to keep a look out where you are going and to taxi slowly—about walking pace, until you are expert at it, anyway. In single-engined aeroplanes it is often impossible to see straight ahead when taxying, because the nose is sticking up in front of you, obscuring the view. It is therefore necessary to steer a zig-zag course over the aerodrome.

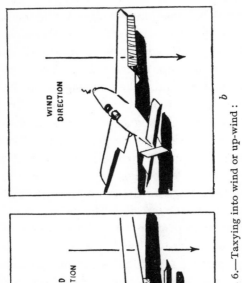

FIG. 6.—Taxying into wind or up-wind :

(a) Straight ahead. Note elevators *up*.
(b) Turning right. Elevators *up*; aileron position reversed with stick to *left*.

As the machine is going so slowly, there is very little air passing over the control surfaces, so that maximum movement must be applied to them to make them in any way effective. Be coarse, therefore, in your movements of the controls. Unless you are taxying down-wind (this will be explained later), always keep the stick back, so that the tail tends to keep on the ground (Fig. 6). Operate the throttle gently—not in big, sudden bursts, because that is bad for the engine, but in slight movements forward and back.

Use the slip-stream of the propeller to advantage. When the engine is revving at 800 revs there is a stronger air-stream operating on the rudder than when it is running at 400 revs. To start a turn, then, put the rudder hard over in the required direction and rev up the engine. As soon as the machine begins to turn, ease back again on the throttle. Come out of the turn by putting the rudder hard over in the opposite direction, and centralise it when your nose is steadied in the desired direction. Because of the sloppy control there is a time-lag before the rudder does its work. You can assist it by taking advantage of the aileron drag, which was explained in the last chapter. To turn to the left, put rudder hard over to left and stick to *right* (at the same time keeping it back in your stomach). To turn right, put rudder hard over to right (right foot forward) and stick over to left.

If you turn too fast, the machine will tip up on to its outside wing-tip, quite possibly damaging the aileron. As soon as you feel this happening, centralise the stick, and minimum damage will be done. Then get out and look at the wing-tip and aileron to see if they have suffered damage.

There is a general tendency when taxying for the aircraft to weathercock into wind, and this must always be borne in mind if full control is to be maintained. If, as is sometimes the case in a high wind, it is not possible to keep the aircraft under control, get a mechanic to hold on to one wing-tip and walk along with you. With his assistance you can steer as you please.

Taxying down-wind is more difficult (Fig. 7), because control, as before, is dependent on air striking the control surfaces from ahead, and therefore the same air speed will necessitate a higher ground speed. Especial care must be taken, therefore, for the aircraft not to get out of hand. It has a lot of momentum, and can do a great deal of damage if, by an error of judgment, its pilot runs it into another machine or some other obstacle. If at any time you see that it *has* got out of control, switch off the engine immediately. This serves the double purpose of depriving it of the pulling power of the engine, even though it may have been only ticking over, and stopping the

propeller, which can do serious damage to itself
and anything it hits if it is still revolving.

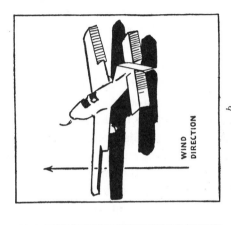

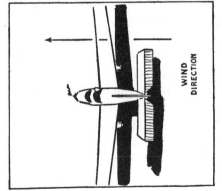

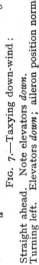

FIG. 7.—Taxying down-wind:

(a) Straight ahead. Note elevators *down*.
(b) Turning left. Elevators *down*; aileron position normal with stick
in direction of turn.

The stick should be held slightly forward, so
that the wind striking the depressed elevator

from the rear will tend to keep the tail on the ground. Only on the occasions when you give the engine a *burst* (move the throttle momentarily forward), in order to provide a strong slip-stream against the rudder so as to make it act as a normal control, should you ease the stick back. This is quite obvious if you think of the conditions a moment. Steering down-wind can be facilitated by moving the stick in *the direction of the turn*— just the opposite way, in fact, to when you are taxying into wind. This helps the turn, because the depressed aileron on the outside wing offers more resistance to the wind coming from the rear than the upturned aileron of the inside wing. The resultant couple helps to turn the machine round in the required direction.

There is a well-established " rule of the road " with which you must comply when taxying an aeroplane on an aerodrome. Keep a good look-out for other aeroplanes coming in to land. As soon as you see that one is approaching, then you must stop, and remain still until it has landed. A moving aeroplane on an aerodrome may well confuse the judgment of the pilot of an incoming machine.

If you find yourself in such a position that you are head on to an obstacle with little room to turn, stop and get out of the cockpit. You will find it is quite easy to lift the tail of your machine round so that you may taxi clear. And never move an inch without making quite certain that there is not a lawn-mower or something else in your way.

CHAPTER III

TAKING OFF

BEFORE taking off, move the stick and rudder-bar to their fullest limit, so as to see that they are working freely and correctly. Accidents have happened in the past, and will continue to happen, because pilots have taken off with controls locked or faultily connected by ground engineers, who are human and liable to make mistakes like everybody else.

The purpose of taking off is to get into the air as quickly and as safely as possible. It is therefore necessary to take off into wind, because the speed at which the aeroplane is air-borne is dependent on air speed. Suppose, for example, the take-off speed (the speed at which the machine is air-borne) is 45 miles an hour, and there is a 20-mile-an-hour wind blowing; by taking off into the wind the ground speed at the moment of take off would be only 25 miles an hour, whereas by taking off down-wind the ground speed would be 65 miles an hour. There are other reasons for taking off into wind which need not be explained here, but which relate to the question of safety.

If you are taking off from an aerodrome, there will be indicators, like a wind-sock or smoke trail, which will tell you the direction of the wind. But if there is no such provision, you must determine the direction of the wind before you get into the plane. Having once determined it, taxi to that position of the aerodrome which will give you the longest run into wind. It is a very good rule always to take off with the maximum distance possible clear ahead of you. Do not, for instance, start your take-off from the middle of the aerodrome, although there may be plenty of room for you to get off. Go to the far boundary, and use the whole aerodrome. By doing this you will have maximum chance of pulling off a successful forced landing in the event of a sudden engine failure. If you use the whole aerodrome, you will be twice as high above the far boundary as if you used only half.

Having arrived at the correct position, take a good look ahead to see that your way is clear, and a look behind to see that no aeroplanes are coming in. If there is one approaching, wait for it to land before you start your take off. See that you are pointing direct into wind.

For taking off (Fig. 8), the trail-trim is put forward to a point about three-quarters along the quadrant. This is to help you with your stick in getting the tail up as you gather speed. Now all is ready.

Push the stick forward as far as it will go, and slowly ease the throttle forward until it will not go any farther. The engine is then giving full power, and you always use full power when taking off. The throttle-lever is so arranged that it will stay in any position it is put, but it is a good idea when taking off to keep your hand on it, so as to be sure that you are getting maximum power from your engine. Otherwise there is just a possibility the lever may slip back a little.

Unless you are careful, the machine will tend to swing as you take off. This is due to over-correction on your part of the rudder. Before you become experienced, you must concentrate really hard on keeping dead straight. Before the machine gathers a lot of speed, the rudder control will be comparatively sloppy—like it is when taxying—but as the speed increases and the air-stream over the rudder increases, less and less movement of the rudder bar is needed to correct the tendency to swing. The simplest way to steer a straight course is to choose some object on the far boundary and steer straight for it (Fig. 9), or you might find it easier to choose some distant cloud. This is sometimes easier, because you can see it without leaning your head out to the side of

the cockpit to look ahead.   The main thing is to
anticipate the nose turning to the right or left,
rather than wait until it has done so and then
putting on a lot of rudder to correct it, which

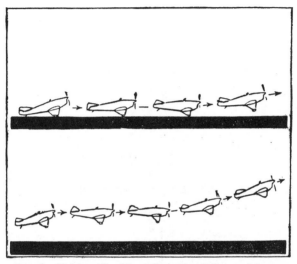

Fig. 8.—Taking-off : The tail rises and the machine runs
along the ground until it has sufficient speed to lift itself
into the air.   It is then flown level with the surface until the
speed is high enough for it to climb away.

probably means starting a swing in the other
direction.   Keep calm and concentrate on keeping
straight, and it will be all right.

The stick movement is such that the machine
gets into *flying position* as soon as possible and
stays there.   The flying position is when the tail

is in such a position that the machine will auto-matically become air-borne when the necessary speed is reached.   If the tail is too high, the nose will be too low, and quite apart from the fact that that position means that the machine is trying to fly into the ground, there is a grave danger of the

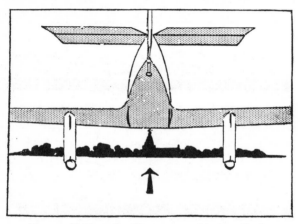

FIG. 9.—Taking off : Choose some object on the far boundary and steer straight for it.

machine nosing over.   If the tail is kept too low, the nose will be pointing in the air instead of being nicely down on the horizon and, although the machine will ultimately stagger off the ground in this position, it will take a long time to do so, and it will be in a dangerous attitude near the stalling-point, and therefore under poor control, which is dangerous. After opening the throttle, keep the stick forward until you feel the tail rise and you are sitting in a level position. Notice the position of the nose relative to some object ahead, and keep it there by gradually easing back on the stick as the speed increases. The faster the air-stream over the elevator becomes, the more sensitive is the control. If the stick therefore is kept too far forward, as the speed increases the nose will drop. If the stick is eased back too quickly, the nose will rise above the datum point I have described. Just ease it gently back, so that the nose stays rock-steady on the horizon all the time, and the machine will automatically lift itself off the ground when flying speed is reached. The gradual cessation of the juddering noise of the *under-carriage* (to which are attached the wheels) as the wings take more and more of the weight until the moment comes when the machine is air-borne is one of the most pleasant sensations in the whole of flying. After the machine has left the ground, keep it flying level a few feet above the ground so that it gains plenty of speed above its stalling speed before you start to climb.

Sometimes circumstances decree that you have to take off across wind, because there is perhaps a high obstacle in your way into wind and you have not enough room to climb over it. The procedure for a cross-wind take-off is similar to a normal take-off, with the exception of the position of the stick. Obviously there will be a tendency for the machine to be blown sideways, and this imposes a sideways strain on the under-carriage. This movement can be considerably reduced by taking off with the wing on the side of the wind being dipped. This has the effect of slipping the machine sideways into wind, which will counteract the skidding caused by the wing. Suppose you are taking off with the wind on your right side; you want to get your right wing down as soon as possible. You therefore start with the stick forward as usual, but instead of having it in the central position, you keep it over on the right side. It is thus in the right-hand forward corner of the cock-pit. Care must be taken not to let the wing-tip touch the ground. Once off the ground, you do a gradual turn into wind.

If the engine fails soon after taking off, the golden rule is to put the stick forward and drop the nose, so as to maintain flying speed, and *glide straight on. Do not succumb to the temptation of turning back onto the aerodrome.* The machine is almost sure to stall and crash if you do. So many accidents have occurred in this way.

CHAPTER IV

FLYING STRAIGHT AND LEVEL

FROM a previous chapter you have learnt the fundamental functions of the controls. Now that we have taxied and taken off, we are in the air, and it is necessary to try the controls in the air. For this reason we will pretend that we have climbed to a safe height and have plenty of room beneath us to recover from any false move.

Take the rudder first. Notice that you have only to put a foot very slightly forward for the nose to start slewing round the horizon. All movements of controls in the air are slight, except in aerobatics, and even then they are smooth and gentle, but firm and sure. Ease your right foot forward slightly—now centralise the rudder again. What happened? So long as your foot was forward the nose slewed round to the right slowly, and stopped pointing in the new direction as soon as you *took off* the rudder (centralised the rudder bar). Now do it again and hold it. First the nose starts slewing round to the right along the horizon; then you notice a wind blowing on your left cheek, because the machine is skidding outwards like a car going round an unbanked turn at speed, then the machine begins to bank to the right, and finally the nose begins to drop below the horizon.

The machine begins to bank because the outside wing on the turn (the left wing in this case) is travelling faster than the inside wing, and therefore gains more lift; and the nose begins to drop because once the aeroplane is banked, it is on a different plane from the horizon, and the rudder still acting in the same direction relative to the aeroplane, forces the nose down below the horizon.

Now the ailerons. We are flying level again, and you ease the stick slightly over to the right. What happens? At the same time as the aeroplane banks to the right (left wing above the right wing), the nose at first slews slightly round to the left and up, because of aileron drag; the aeroplane *side-slips* to the right because you have not used any rudder to give it a turning movement; and then the nose falls because the lift behind the centre of gravity is greater than in front of it.

Now the elevator. This is very simple. Ease the stick slightly back and the nose rises above the horizon, slightly forward and it sinks below the horizon. If you keep the stick back too long, the aeroplane will reach a stalled attitude with its nose high in the air and having lost most of its speed. Just like a car, it will only climb a limited gradient. If you hold the stick forward, the aeroplane will dive steeper and steeper and faster and faster until you start easing back on the stick again and bringing the nose up onto the horizon, whence once again it will settle down to level flight.

Roughly speaking, the position of the throttle for normal cruising is about three-quarters of the way forward. You climb off the aerodrome at full throttle, and then, when you are well clear of any possible obstruction, you ease back the throttle a quarter of the way. When you wish to lose height, you ease it back still farther, so that the engine does not race and the speed of the aircraft is kept down to reasonable proportions. An aeroplane losing height has the same peculiarities as a car going downhill.

Before trying to fly straight and level (Fig. 10), take a look around you. Notice that your view around you is divided into two halves : that which is above the horizon, and that which is below. The horizon stretches right around you. In fact it is a circle of which you are the centre. For this reason, any point of it can be used as a guide to fly straight. Whatever your height above the

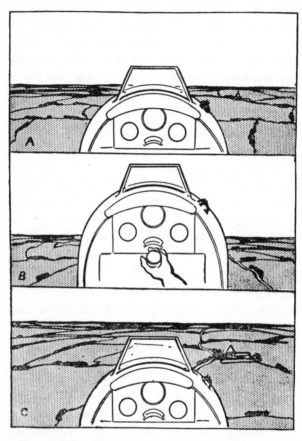

FIG. 10.—Keep the nose *on the horizon* when flying level, as in A, not *above* as in B (which is climbing), or below as in C (which is gliding).

earth, a line joining you to the horizon is roughly
a tangent to the curve of the earth. The horizon
can therefore be used as a guide to fly level.
Similarly, by aligning the wings to the horizon,
you can keep the plane flying level laterally.

You will have realised by now that there are
two planes in which to fly level—the lateral plane
and the longitudinal plane. To fly level laterally
you see that one wing is not lower than the other.
If it is, pull it up by moving the stick away from
it. And to fly level longitudinally, you keep some
point of the nose on the horizon by easing the
stick forward or backward, as the case may be.
Remember always to hold the stick lightly in the
right hand. *Do not grip it.*

A certain amount of practice is required before
you can fly level longitudinally, because the mark
on the aeroplane which you align with some point
on the horizon is different for every aeroplane
and for differing speeds of the same aeroplane.

First let us assume that you are flying along
level at cruising speed—about 100 miles an hour—
that is, with the throttle three-quarters of the way
forward. Take a look at the altimeter and note
your height. Then fly the machine at what you
think is level flight. If the nose is too low, the
machine will gain speed and lose height. The
latter you determine by the altimeter. If you

have settled the nose too high, then the machine will lose speed and gain height. By keeping the throttle in the same position, therefore, and by watching the air-speed indicator and the altimeter, you will be able to find the proper attitude of the machine for flying level.

Very soon you will be able to determine this position without even glancing at the instruments. An experienced pilot can fly a new plane for the first time and have no difficulty in finding the level position. He can tell by the change of engine note if he is losing or gaining speed, and by the general feel of the aeroplane if he is flying level.

You want to learn to place as little reliance as possible on your instruments. Sometimes they go wrong, and probably in a moment of emergency you will have no time to look at them. So learn to fly your aeroplane by *feel*. This is not as vague as it sounds, but entirely practical. While you are practising flying level I will explain this.

You have realised by now that the faster your speed, the harder it is to move the controls and the less movement is necessary to get the required result. There is therefore a direct relationship between the feel of the controls and the speed of the aeroplane. This relationship is there without qualification for the ailerons; but the elevator and rudder, being behind the propeller, and therefore in its slip-stream, are affected not only by the speed of the aeroplane, but also whether the engine is on or off or revving fast or slow.   The ailerons are well outside the slip-steam.   For this reason, it is on the aileron control that a pilot depends for his feel.

When the aeroplane is flying near its stalling speed, you will find that the aileron control is very sloppy.   You can literally waggle the stick from side to side of the cockpit with very little effect. When the aeroplane is flying fast, the aileron control has stiffened up, and you can only move the stick a little way.   It feels quite firm.   Here, then, is a perfectly accurate way for the pilot to determine at any time without any reference to instruments how near he is flying to his stalling point (the point at which the wings lose their lift and the aeroplane as a result drops out of control), and therefore how near to the danger point he is.

In order to make full use of this ready-to-hand safety measure, get into the habit of feeling your aileron control under all conditions of flight. If you do this, your reaction in an emergency will be instantaneous, and may well prevent an accident.

CHAPTER V

STALLING, CLIMBING AND GLIDING

THE most vital speed, from the pilot's point of view, of an aeroplane is its stalling speed. This is because it is the speed at which the machine ceases to become air-borne and is therefore out of control. An aeroplane that has stalled always loses height (perhaps 200 or 300 feet) before sufficient speed has been regained for it to again become controllable. If it stalls near the ground, it will therefore hit the ground before the pilot has been able to regain control, and a serious accident results. It is for this reason that you see so often that a fatal accident was due to the machine stalling. It stalls just the same way high up, but does not result in an accident, because there is sufficient height for the pilot to recover in.

As it is so vital, it is most necessary for a pilot to be very familiar with the symptoms that precede a stall, so that he may avoid it. When you are flying a new aeroplane, therefore, one of the first things to do is to climb to a really safe height and deliberately stall it, so that you know just what the symptoms of that particular aeroplane are.

The way to do this is simple. When you have gained at least 2000 feet of height, and are flying straight and level, ease back the throttle as far as it will go, so that the engine is just ticking over, and at the same time ease back the stick so that the nose points above the horizon. The machine will quickly lose speed. As it does so, feel your ailerons in the manner described above, and notice how they become more and more sloppy. At the actual point of stall you are able to waggle the stick from side to side in the cockpit, and it will have no effect. Another thing that happens as the speed drops is that the nose will appear to be becoming more and more heavy, so that, in order to keep it above the horizon, you will have to increase the pressure on the stick to keep it back. This you do at the same time as wagging it from side to side. At the point of the stall the machine appears to hang suspended and still in the air. After what seems to be a complete pause in movement, the nose suddenly drops, in spite of the fact that your stick is as far back as it can be (Fig. 11). This is because the point of stall has been reached and your controls are useless. In the old days machines used to do funny things when they stalled, but modern machines rarely do anything

C

else than just drop their nose and perhaps one wing. To regain control, all you do is to ease the stick forward, and the machine will gather speed again, and with the increase in speed, your control will be regained. If you do not ease the stick forward, the natural action of the stalled machine

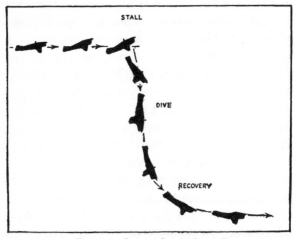

FIG. 11.—Into and out of a stall.

dropping its nose will result in sufficient speed being regained for your elevator to take effect again, so that almost immediately the nose will rise again, and this will result in a second stall.

You want to practise a stall several times, not only so that you get used to the feel of the controls before the point of stall is reached so that you can avoid it when necessary, but also because it will be your first taste of mild aerobatics, and the peculiar feeling of inanimate suspension which you get at the point of a deliberate stall will give you confidence once you become used to it ; or, rather, your ability to show that it is nothing dangerous and you can get out of it will give you confidence.

So much for stalling. The next thing to learn is climbing (Fig. 10), and this is something quite near to stalling, but must be kept at a distance.

Every kind of aeroplane has different climbing characteristics. But whatever your aeroplane, the best climbing speed is that which raises the aeroplane the greatest height in the shortest distance. Even two aeroplanes of the same type can have different climbing speeds, due to their being rigged slightly differently. To determine the best climbing speed, fly straight and level, and then gently ease back the stick, at the same time easing forward the throttle, because you want more power from the engine for climbing. When the nose has risen a little way above the horizon, keep it there by correct movement of the stick. You will notice that the machine loses speed. You will see this by the A.S.I. (air-speed indicator), and you will also hear the engine losing revs. As this happens, ease the stick from side to side so as to feel your aileron control. If the ailerons begin to feel sloppy, then you are trying to climb at too steep an angle for maximum efficiency, so ease the stick forward a trifle and continue the climb with the nose not quite so high above the horizon. The attitude of the machine at which you just feel a nice, firm aileron control is the best climbing angle. When you have determined this, you can read off the speed from the A.S.I. Do not be misled by the fact that you can fly with the nose higher without the machine stalling. You can certainly do this, but the machine is squashing its way through the air, and is not climbing nearly so fast as when the nose is a little lower. You will find that the best climbing speed of your machine which cruises at 100 miles an hour is somewhere in the region of 70 miles an hour. I hope that from this description it is clear to you that the climbing angle of an aeroplane is the angle between the longitudinal axis of the aeroplane and the horizontal. The best climbing angle is that at which the best rate of climb is maintained. I should perhaps mention that the best climbing angle differs according to your engine revs—in other words, according to the position of your throttle. But unless you are going to climb thousands of feet, when the strain on the engine will become severe, you can always climb at full throttle. Particularly important is this when you are taking off, as you want to get as high as you can as quickly as you can. This gives more chance to choose an area of ground in which to land in the event of sudden engine failure. When you have reached 1000 feet or so, and still want to go on climbing, then you can ease back the throttle a little and continue the climb at slightly reduced power. Although the best climbing angle differs according to throttle setting, the best climbing speed, for all practical purposes, remains the same.

As already explained, the density of the air gets less and less the higher you go. This means that oxygen becomes more and more scarce, with the result that the engine loses power as height is gained. The aeroplane climbs at a slower and slower rate, because the reserve of engine-power over and above that which is required just to keep it flying level gets less and less. Finally a point is reached when there is just enough power to keep it flying level and none to make it climb. The height at which this occurs is called the *ceiling* of the aircraft, and in the case of our training aeroplane is somewhere around 20,000 feet. It can be readily understood that when this state of affairs is reached, the attitude of the machine is its best climbing angle, although it is only being successful in flying level. It will take about an hour and a quarter for you to reach the ceiling of your aircraft, steadily climbing at the best angle all the while. Whatever the aircraft, the time taken to reach its ceiling is nearly the same.

The next thing for you to learn is how to glide. Gliding is often erroneously described as flying with engine off. It is, in fact, flying with engine throttled right down so that it is idling at minimum revs. The engine would only be " off " if you cut the switches, but these you do not touch. The reason that it is wrongly described is no doubt due to the contrast of the roar of the engine when at cruising revs and its silence when it is just ticking over on a glide. If the engine fails and cuts of its own accord, then of course gliding is flying with engine off, but this is an involuntary procedure.

You have learnt that when climbing you are seeking to *gain* as much height as possible for horizontal distance covered. When gliding you seek to lose as *little* height as possible for horizontal distance covered. This generalisation, like every other one, is liable to modification, but in the main it is true. A pilot throttles back his engine and glides in order to lose height without gaining unnecessary speed. If, owing to a breakdown, his engine cuts out, then he glides in order to maintain flying speed without engine. He merely calls upon gravity to supply the power to keep him in the air at all, and pays for it by losing height.   He is, however, under full control all the time.

In many respects gliding is similar to climbing. The gliding angle is the angle between the horizontal axis of the aircraft and the horizontal level, and the pilot maintains his gliding angle by keeping the nose in a set position in relation to the horizon (Fig. 10).   But instead of the angle and the nose being above the horizontal level or horizon, as in climbing, it is below them.   The best gliding speed of an aircraft is determined in a similar way to the best climbing speed, and this is in direct relation to the best gliding angle.

In order to start a glide, throttle back as far as the throttle lever will go, and ease the nose down a similar distance below the horizon as it was above it for climbing.   The speed of the aircraft will soon decrease, and, if you have set the machine at the correct angle, it will settle down to a steady speed round about 70 miles an hour.   If the nose is too high, the speed will drop further, and you will feel your aileron control becoming sloppy. As soon as this happens, ease the stick forward; the nose will drop, and the speed will be regained. If you put the nose too far below the horizon, the speed will rise unduly, and, as usual, you will be able to detect this by the stiffening of the controls, as well as by a glance at the A.S.I.   A steep glide is termed a dive, and is an inefficient way of losing height, in that the machine will traverse a comparatively short horizontal distance for height lost.   What you must be very careful about in gliding is that you do not glide too slow.   You want to have a good margin of speed above the stalling speed in order to have full control.   On rough days you must glide faster than usual, in order to be certain of having control under sudden changes of air conditions.   I need hardly say that an aeroplane will stall with engine off in just the same way as it does with engine on, if its pilot allows it to lose flying speed by keeping its nose too far up.

The chief use for the glide is for approaching down on to an aerodrome preparatory to landing. On the other hand, it is at its greatest value when an engine cut necessitates a pilot making a forced landing without the safeguard of engine power to call on.

CHAPTER VI

TURNING

IN order to appreciate the problems involved in the matter of turning an aeroplane, think for a moment of a motor-car. If you take a bend in a flat level road too fast, there is a tendency for the car to skid outwards and overturn. Race tracks, like Brooklands, overcome this tendency by having banked turns, the track being level on the inside and becoming steeper and steeper as the outside of the turn is reached. A car taking the turn slowly keeps on the inside, but one which is going fast takes the corner high up the banking—just how high up depending on its speed and the gradient of the track. Alternatively, the driver may choose his position on the banking and then adjust his speed accordingly. If his speed is adjusted to the banking correctly, he can take the corner with perfect ease, there being no tendency for his car to skid outwards. Supposing he takes the banking too high for the speed he is travelling, then there will be a tendency for his car to slip in or down the slope.

Exactly the same thing happens with an aeroplane, but instead of the pilot flying along a track which is banked, he himself, by means of his aileron control, banks his aeroplane according to his rate of turn. If he banks too much for his rate of turn, the aeroplane will slip sideways; but if he does not bank enough, then his aeroplane will skid outwards. Alternatively, suppose he puts his aeroplane into a set degree of bank and turns too slow, it will slip inwards; and if he turns too fast,

FIG. 12.—Into and out of a turn.

it will skid outwards. Both these mistakes are very easily recognised by a pilot. If his machine is slipping inwards on a left-hand turn, for example, he feels a draught on his left cheek, and if it is skidding outwards, he feels a draught on his outside, or right, cheek, at the same time feeling a distinct tendency for him to be thrown against the inside (or left side) of the cockpit.

The effect of the controls on a banked aeroplane is a little confusing at first. The golden rule is to remember that, *relative to the aeroplane*, they work the same. When you ease the stick back, whatever the position of the aeroplane relative to the horizon, the nose always rises in a sort of endeavour to catch its tail; when you put on left rudder (left foot forward) the nose will always turn towards the left wing-tip, and when you put on right rudder it will always try to turn towards the right wing-tip. If you bear that in mind, you will have no difficulty in understanding the control movements for going into, holding, and coming out of turns (Fig. 12).

Before trying a turn, think purely theoretically of the function of the elevator and rudder under the two extremes of bank—full bank (90 degrees to the horizon) and no bank (wings parallel to the horizon). You know what happens in the latter case. Ease the stick back and up goes the nose, put on rudder and the nose slews round the horizon towards the inside wing-tip. Now, then, let us assume that the aeroplane is theoretically suspended in the sky, flying along with full bank on— that is, with its wings at 90 degrees to the horizon. What happens when you ease the stick back? The nose still tries to reach over your head and catch its tail; but because the wings are at right angles to the horizon, *the nose slews round the horizon.* In other words, the elevator has the same effect on the nose relative to the horizon as the rudder has when the aeroplane is flying level (Fig. 13).

When you put rudder on in this fully banked

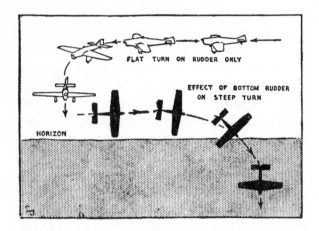

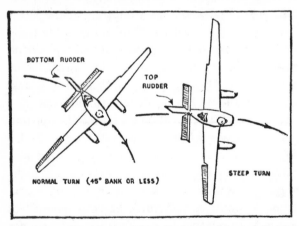

Fig. 13.—When the machine is banked, rudder and elevator tend to exchange functions. This effect increases progressively until at 90° bank the rudder becomes an elevator and the elevator a rudder.

position, the nose still tries to turn towards the wing-tip, but because the wing is at right angles to the horizon, the nose actually moves directly above or below the horizon, according to whether you put on *top rudder* (right foot forward in a left bank, left foot forward in a right bank) or *bottom rudder* (right foot forward in a right bank or left foot forward in a left bank). Intermediate angles of bank within these two limits call for compromise between elevator and rudder.

A good rule when turning is always to settle on an angle of bank and adjust your rate of turn to that angle, rather than settle on a rate of turn and adjust your angle of bank to that.

Bearing that in mind, let us try a gentle turn to the left. Ease the stick over to the left a little way. This immediately puts on a little left bank. At the same time put on a little left rudder to start the turn to the left. Because the machine has left bank on it, the nose will tend to drop, and the left rudder will also tend to drop the nose a little below the horizon, as well as slew it round because the machine is on a tilted plane. You therefore counteract this by easing back on the stick a little, which has the effect of lifting the nose up on to the horizon again, but it also has the effect of helping to turn the machine. As the bank increases, so the rudder loses its turning effect and assumes the rôle of elevator, and so the elevator loses its " elevating " effect and assumes the rôle of steering control.   But on this first turn we do not wish to do a steep bank or anything like it.   When you have got 10 degrees of bank on, adjust the stick so that the bank does not get any steeper.   I say " adjust the stick " advisedly, because you might think that this end is achieved by centralising the stick.   In actual fact you will have to keep the stick a little over to the right, in order to prevent the bank increasing.   This is because the right wing (the outside wing of the turn) is travelling faster than the inside wing, and therefore gaining more lift.   Consequently, if you were to centralise the stick in a turn, the bank would get steeper and steeper.   You therefore always have to move it a little over the central position, in order to *hold off* the bank.

You must keep the nose just above the horizon in the same way as flying level.   If you let it drop too low, the machine will gain speed and lose height.   You pull it up again by adjustment of the elevator and rudder in the manner described above.   If it gets too high, the machine will lose speed, and you must bring it down again to the mean position on the horizon.

You can maintain the correct rate of turn by your sense of balance.   If you are turning too slow for the amount of bank you have on, you will feel the machine slipping inwards (and a draught on your inside cheek), and if your rate of turn is too fast for the bank, you will feel the machine skidding outwards (and a draught on your outside cheek). Always remember that it is better to have too *much* bank rather than too *little.*

The inclinometer—that curved spirit-level at the top of your dashboard—will tell you quite definitely if your banks and rate of turn are in correct relation to one another. At first, until you have experienced the feeling of slipping in and skidding out, it is advisable to seek guidance from your inclinometer. In a perfectly balanced turn, however steep, the bubble will be in the centre of the level. If your rate of turn is too slow for the bank you have on, the bubble will move towards the outside of the turn; if the rate of turn is too fast for the bank you have on, the bubble will move towards the inside of the turn. In order to get it central again, keep the bank constant and adjust the rate with your elevator and rudder in correct proportion by maintaining the nose in the right position above the horizon. The inclinometer is especially useful in rough weather, when the machine can be jumping about all over the place, making accurate turns by " feel " difficult.

When you want to come out of the turn, apply opposite bank and rudder together. You will find that more pressure is required on the controls coming out than when going into a turn. As you take off the bank, so you must adjust your rudder in order to be properly balanced all the while; otherwise the machine will skid or slip coming out of the turn in just the same way as it will when in the turn, and the rate is not adjusted to the bank. Care must be taken to keep the nose on the same position on the horizon as before. This is again done by a combination of elevator and rudder; the more the bank is taken off, the less the turning effect to the elevator and the more the rudder, until, when the machine is level again and there is no bank, the elevator and rudder assume once more the normal functions in level flight.

Now try a steep turn. By steep turn I mean anything over 50 degrees of bank. Until you are used to it, you will imagine that you are doing a 90-degree banked turn when in reality you are doing one much less steep, because the unusual attitude of the machine on its side is misleading.

To make it easier to understand, assume that you are doing a turn with 90 degrees of bank. In actual fact you would not attempt this until you were well practised in less steep turns. But when your machine has 90 degrees of bank on, you can follow that the rudder becomes the elevator completely and the elevator becomes the rudder. In other words, the only way to adjust the position of the nose on the horizon is by altering the rudder, and the only way to adjust your

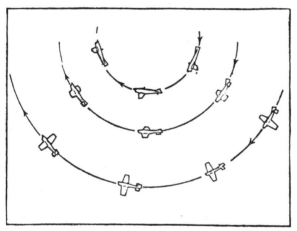

Fig. 14.—Different rates of turn showing attitude of machine and path followed, viewed from above.

rate of turn is by means of the elevator. When in this position you can easily understand the meaning of the terms top and bottom rudder, which are used when referring to rudder movements in a turn.

Obviously, when the machine is banked at 90 degrees, it is in position for maximum rate of turn (Fig. 14). This is obtained by holding the stick well back, and quite a lot of force is required to do this. If it is not held back far enough, the rate of turn will be too slow, and the machine will slip violently inwards. The sensation for the pilot in a steep turn requires some getting used to, because centrifugal force is forcing him into his seat and the blood is being forced away from his head. It is under these conditions, if his movement has been too violent, and his rate of turn consequently too fast, that he may experience what is commonly known as a " black-out ". A black-out is when his brain has been drained of blood, and is a good warning, incidentally, that he is imposing too heavy a strain on the structure of the aeroplane.

What is most important to remember is that the stalling speed of an aeroplane increases with the amount of bank used in a turn. The stalling speed of an aeroplane flying level may be 50 miles an hour, but when it is in a 90-degree banked turn it is probably about 85 miles an hour. For this reason, when you do a steep turn, *always use more throttle*, and if you are going to hold it for a complete turn, have the throttle as far open as it will go. Do not try to hold a really steep turn for more than a complete turn (360 degrees), because the machine will have lost too much speed by then to be safe to continue. But you can get over this if circumstances are such that you are able to lose a little height with impunity by keeping the nose a bit below the horizon. This will keep your speed up. Do not try to do this before you are really experienced, because, if you do, you are looking for trouble. The ability to hold a really steep turn for any length of time is one of the most difficult manœuvres in flying.

When practising turns, do not get into the habit of always turning in the same direction. You will find, if you are right-handed, it is easier to do turns to the left, and to do them to the right requires much more concentration. If you are going to favour one turn above the other, favour the right-hand turn. If you get proficient in that you will automatically be proficient in the other.

Another important thing to remember is: never assume that you have the sky to yourself. Before you make a turn, always look around in the direction you are going to turn to see that there are no other aircraft near. One is very much inclined to think that the sky is so large that the risk of collision is infinitesimal, but collisions do happen, and are very much worth guarding against! On two occasions in my experience I have *heard* an aeroplane flash past me before I saw it, and on each occasion I was flying on a steady course. The other man was, too, and because our aircraft each had no view ahead, we did not see each other. Fortunately, instead of meeting head-on, we were flying on different levels, and just missed one another. But that shows that one can never assume that one has the sky to oneself. If you are flying an aeroplane from which you cannot see right ahead (only *modern*, light, single-engined machines, unbelievably enough, make this possible), it is worth while to slew the nose round a little every now and then, just to make sure that your way ahead is clear.

Coming out of a steep turn requires a lot of practice before you can do it smoothly with correct synchronisation of controls to avoid slipping or skidding, but if you concentrate hard, you will not find it too difficult. However, never be satisfied unless you come out quite cleanly, with the nose steady on the horizon all the time and rudder and elevator doing their job with precision.

Climbing and gliding turns are almost the same as level-flight turns, the only difference being in the attitude of the machine relative to the horizon. But because of the stalling speed in a turn being higher than when the machine has no bank on, great care must be taken that you are either climbing or gliding with ample speed.

A climbing turn must be made with more speed than you use when just climbing, and you cannot normally do steep climbing turns because of the rapid loss of speed. A golden rule is never to do climbing turns near the ground. So often accidents have happened by a pilot taking off from an aerodrome flushed with exuberance and the desire to show off, and making a climbing turn too soon. He stalls, and has no height in which to recover. This happens over and over again. Do not therefore try to emulate the experienced stunt pilot whom you have seen doing this spectacular manœuvre at flying meetings. He can do it safely. You cannot. Even he is asking for trouble if his engine suddenly fails.

The same thing applies to gliding turns. Better far to have too much speed than too little; and do not do them too near the ground. Because the engine is throttled back in a glide, the elevator and rudder will not be so sensitive, so that coarser movements will be required to get the desired result. This need not bother you. Just move the controls firmly but gently always so far as to get the desired result. Before going in to a gliding turn, lower the nose slightly to get the little extra desired speed for a safe turn, and then ease it up again when you have completed the turn.

And always feel your ailerons in all these manœuvres, so that you can be automatically sure that you are not dangerously near the stalling speed.

Gliding is among the most pleasant sensations of flying. Free of the roar of the engine, it is a delight to glide smoothly down invisible paths in the air, and especially is it a delight to choose a day when there are fat, billowy, isolated clouds, and to glide in the valleys that they form, their great forms towering high on either side of one. But if you glide for more than 1000 feet at a time, give the engine a burst of throttle every now and then so as to keep it warm.

CHAPTER VII

APPROACHING AND LANDING

Now you come to the most difficult part of your course of flying instruction—approaching and landing. It is difficult because it cannot be done without perfect judgment, and judgment only comes with experience. So many times a pupil does everything very well in the air, but when he comes to learn how to land, nothing seems to go right, and he gets discouraged. I always found that it took more time to teach a pupil how to land (up to the stage only when he could go solo) than it took for him to learn everything else— turning, gliding, climbing, taking-off, spinning, etc. You require great patience and a will of iron, and then everything will be all right. But do not expect to learn how to approach and land as easily as you have learnt everything else.

As I have stated before, I am teaching you in this book the various evolutions in the proper sequence of flight. In other words, we have gone through together how to fly an aeroplane from the time you get into it outside the hangar to the time you land it. In real life you will not learn in that sequence, because some evolutions are more difficult than those that follow them, and therefore you are taught the later ones first. But in a book of instruction there is no necessity for one to switch about. It merely makes it confusing, and not so interesting. However, we have now come to the stage when our instruction conforms to the sequence of real-life instruction. From now on we travel a parallel course to the course which you will be given when you are really learning to fly.

When you have come to the end of a flight and it is time to land, take a look over the side at the aerodrome. It looks mighty small, doesn't it? No wonder, then, that much practice is required in judging your glide down so that your wheels touch down just where you want them to. At first you can but be content with alighting on the aerodrome, but later on you *must* not be content with anything else but landing within a few yards of a previously selected point. If you always try to do this, you may be sure that you have the maximum chance of pulling off a successful forced landing, when the rare occasion arises, in a field of limited space. Besides, it is a grand game to play, compared to which any other is child's play. The satisfaction of gently alighting an aeroplane on a predetermined spot must be experienced to be believed.

Just where one lands is dependent on judgment of the approach. An aeroplane always lands at the same speed which is the speed at which it stalls. The approach has therefore to be made so that this stalling speed is reached immediately above the point at which you want to alight. And when I say " above ", I do not mean hundreds of feet above. I mean 6 *inches* above. You have already learnt what an aeroplane does when it stalls in the air. It does exactly the same when you land it; but as it is only a few inches above the ground, it sinks those few inches, and its weight is taken by the ground-surface. If you misjudge your landing, and instead of there being only a few inches between wheels and ground at the moment of stall there are a few feet, the machine will drop heavily onto the ground and probably sustain damage to its structure.

The approach is always made into wind. The first thing to do, therefore, is to find out the direction of the wind. This is easily done by looking at the windsock on the aerodrome, but you should always bear in mind the direction of the wind during a flight, so that you are prepared for any sudden landing (Fig. 22). Smoke-stacks are the most satisfactory means for checking up on wind direction.

There are a number of ways of making an

approach; the best way, unfortunately, is now impracticable for landing on any aerodrome but rarely used ones, because it entails contravening the " rule of the road ". You can only fly round the perimeter of an aerodrome in one way. Generally this is anti-clockwise, which is called a left-hand circuit; but some R.A.F. aerodromes have right-hand circuits. The method of approach to which I refer involves a series of " S " turns, first to the right and then to the left, so that if you approach like this, you inevitably contravene the circuit regulations. It is, however, an excellent method for approaching onto fields, etc., so I will leave the explanation of it until the chapter on forced landings.

The normal approach is started at about 1000 feet. This means that you place the machine in a favourable position to alight on the aerodrome from 1000 feet with engine throttled back and the machine in a glide. You can appreciate that the machine will cover more ground gliding into a five-mile-an-hour wind while losing 1000 feet of height than it will gliding with a 20-mile-an-hour wind against it. Every approach is therefore different, and adjustment of position has to be made according to the strength of wind. If you start your approach at right angles to the wind and glide down a path parallel to the boundary of the

aerodrome but about 400 yards behind it, you
give yourself a margin for error (Fig. 15). At any
time during the glide down that path you can turn
into wind and still land on the aerodrome. If you
are too high to start with, you continue to glide
down, losing height until you are sure you can get

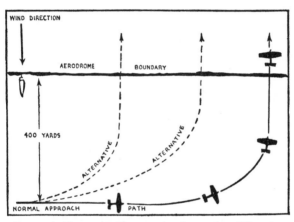

FIG. 15.—Give yourself a margin of error by gliding down
a path about 400 yards outside and parallel to the aerodrome
boundary at right-angles to the wind.

into the aerodrome; but if you are comparatively
low to start with, you turn into wind immediately
you become abreast of the aerodrome. Between
these two limits is allowance for a healthy margin
of error.

The great thing to avoid in the approach is
under-shooting (finding yourself at the last moment

without enough height to get into the aerodrome without a burst of engine). This is a very common fault with beginners, who always tend to under-shoot. The remedy is to turn in to the aerodrome when you estimate that you will touch down at the far hedge. If you did do this, and hit the far hedge, the result would naturally be disastrous; but you can be pretty sure that you will have touched down long before this, because of the tendency to under-shoot. Later on, when you have become practised in this difficult art, the point on the aerodrome to aim for is about one-third the way across it. You can always lose height by side-slipping (you will learn this later on), but you can never regain height without engine. In a forced landing you have no engine, so that it is essential for you to become accustomed to judge every approach you make onto an aero-drome without calling on the engine to get you out of a difficulty. On the other hand, if you find that you *have* misjudged it and you are under-shooting, have no hesitation in giving a powerful and sus-tained burst of engine to get you over the hedge. Again there is a tremendous urge to try to scrape over the hedge without this saving burst of engine. If you succumb to this, then the machine will stall and you will find yourself in a sorry mess the wrong side of the hedge, if not actually in it.

Presumably this urge to avoid using the engine in such a position is due to the fact that it is an acknowledgment of failure to judge the approach properly, and also to the contempt with which pilots are inclined to treat a man who has to *rumble* (use his engine at the last moment). Pay no attention to those who scoff at you. The experienced pilot will commend you for having the sense to acknowledge a mistake and to use your engine to get out of its consequences. But you must not make a habit of it.

Always during your approach keep a sharp look-out for other aircraft, because the vicinity of an aerodrome is always where you find most aircraft. Glide down at a good speed—about 75 miles an hour—and as soon as you have shut off your engine to begin the glide, ease back the tail-trim so that the stick is light in your hand. If you do not do this, you will find the machine nose-heavy, and the pressure on the stick necessary to keep the nose up is apt to be confusing as well as tiring.

Now we come to landing. We assume that you have judged your approach correctly, so that when you are about 400 feet up you have turned into wind and are coming down in a nice, steady, straight glide, which will result in the aircraft touching down in the centre of the aerodrome.

If you find that you have misjudged the approach in such a way that a last-minute turn close to the ground is necessary, then put your engine full on, fly across the aerodrome, gaining height again, and make another circuit.   Indeed, whenever you are in the slightest doubt about your judgment, play for safety and do another circuit.   You can go on doing this quite happily until your petrol gives out, which will probably be a long time ahead.   Incidentally, always keep an eye on your petrol-gauge, so that you are not caught napping with an empty tank.   The gauge is either on the dashboard or on the wing, easily visible from the cockpit.

The essence of landing is to glide down at an angle to the ground, and then, when within a few feet of the surface, to change the angle to flight along a path 6 inches to 1 foot above the ground and parallel to it (Fig. 16).   I nearly wrote " level flight ", but the path is not level when the aerodrome surface is on an incline.   It must always be parallel to the surface.   The machine must proceed along this path until it loses speed to such an extent that its stalling speed is reached and it will sink the 6 inches to make a perfect landing.   That is the essence of landing.

I have deliberately omitted aerodynamical explanations in this book, as the student who wishes to delve into this science must do so in text-books written for the specialist. I have only referred to aerodynamic factors in so far as they are part and parcel of piloting a machine. But we now come to a phenomenon regarding an aeroplane in flight which must be briefly explained.

Very broadly speaking, the lift derived by an aeroplane is dependent upon two things. The first is speed, and the second is the *angle of incidence* of the wings. The angle of incidence is sometimes called the angle of attack of the wings, and it is the angle they make with the direction of air-stream. When the nose of the aeroplane is raised, this angle of incidence is increased; when depressed, the angle is decreased. Now we come to the point with regard to landing. In order to fly level at, say, 75 miles an hour, the angle of incidence is less than it is to fly level at 50 miles an hour. The loss of lift due to the slower

FIG. 16.—A perfect three-point landing. Machine flies 6 inches to a foot above the aerodrome surface until flying speed has been lost and then sinks to the ground, alighting on wheels and tail-skid together.

speed has to be compensated for by the increase in the angle of incidence.

It is therefore apparent that, in order to fly along the parallel path to the surface of the aerodrome when landing, the pilot must gradually increase the angle of incidence of the wings as the speed decreases. If he does this correctly, the nose will be as high up as his elevator can get it at the moment when his machine has reached stalling point, and the machine will settle comfortably on the ground, his stick as far back as it will go into the pit of his stomach.

If he eases his stick back too quickly, the machine will climb away from the ground; and if he does not do it quick enough, the wheels will touch down prematurely, with the tail still in the air. For an absolutely correct landing, wheels and tail-skid touch the ground simultaneously in a *three-point landing*.

If the pilot fails to ease the stick back quickly enough and the wheels touch before the machine has lost flying speed, the machine will in all probability *balloon* into the air and adopt a dangerous attitude (Fig. 17). On touching the ground, the wheels will bounce, thus immediately and suddenly increasing the angle of incidence of the wings by bouncing the nose into the air. Because the machine still has flying speed, this sudden increase in incidence will cause it to do a sudden climb, resulting quite possibly in a stall 10 feet or so above the ground. Whatever happens, then, a pilot must not try to force his machine to settle on the ground. It will not do so until it has lost flying speed, and any sudden movement of the stick back will result in the machine ballooning. Thus it can be seen that there is only one way to do a landing, and that is to judge it perfectly.

The steady approach down on to the aerodrome that I have advocated is necessary so that you can have plenty of time to see that you are landing dead into wind. The wind-sock on the aerodrome will only tell you the approximate direction. Final adjustment has to be made as you glide

D

Fig. 17.—" Ballooning " : Machine has touched down on its wheels before flying speed was lost and has bounced into the air at an angle which immediately produces a stall.

down when you notice that you are drifting to one side or the other. If you see that you are drifting to the left—that is, the machine is moving bodily sideways to the left—you cannot be pointing directly into wind. Put on a little right rudder, so that the nose points into the wind. You can tell how far to turn by looking at the ground and steering straight as soon as you see that you have no drift. For these last-minute adjustments it is best not to put on bank, but to do a gentle *flat turn*.

You will probably find that it is best to look out of the cockpit to the left and ahead. It is more comfortable than looking out to the right. However, you must not forget occasionally to cast your eyes out of the right side of the cockpit to see that the way is clear.

Fix your eyes on a point as far to the front as possible and about 20 yards ahead. If you look at the ground too close to you, the surface is a blur, and it is consequently difficult to judge your landing.

Having changed your glide down into flight parallel to the surface of the aerodrome, *hold off* the machine by gradually easing back the stick until it gently stalls onto the ground. You can appreciate that, as you are flying to such fine limits above the ground when landing, there is no

scope whatever for mistakes, and it is for this
reason that landing takes so long to learn. You
can turn inaccurately and get away with it, but
you can never land inaccurately without damage
to the machine.

If you glide down too fast, you will use up a lot
of the aerodrome before the machine loses speed
sufficiently to stall.   Take care, then, to keep your
glide down to the correct speed, and do not forget
to feel your ailerons, so that you are independent
of instruments to tell you your speed.

When you are learning and practising after you
have gone solo, there will be many occasions when
you fail to judge the landing properly.   Either
you will not hold off long enough, and the wheels
will touch down too soon, perhaps causing the
machine to balloon, or you will hold off too long
and too high, and you will find yourself suspended
ominously near the stall feet above the ground
instead of inches.   On any such occasion put the
throttle forward and go round again.   But do
not try climbing straight away.   Fly level above
the ground until the machine has gathered
sufficient speed for climbing.

If you find that you are going to *over-shoot*
(misjudged your approach by having too much
height to get into the aerodrome), then you can
get rid of surplus height by *side-slipping* (Fig. 18).

Side-slipping is merely a way to make the machine thoroughly inefficient, and therefore to steepen the gliding angle *without increasing the speed*. The way to side-slip is to put on bank and *opposite* rudder—just the reverse of what you do in a turn. But you must be careful that you lower the nose a

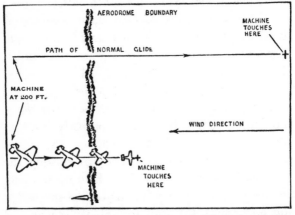

FIG. 18.—Comparison between normal glide path and glide shortened by side-slipping off height, thus making possible a longer landing run.

little when you go into the side-slip, so as to increase slightly the forward speed of the machine and keep it well above the stalling-point. You so adjust the elevator and rudder controls that the nose of the machine remains pointing in the same direction that it was when gliding normally. You keep just enough opposite rudder on to prevent the nose turning round in the direction of the bank, and enough elevator to keep it at the normal gliding angle.

A very useful way of losing speed when you find that you have surplus speed after flattening out is by *swish-tailing* (Fig. 19). Once again, this is a way of deliberately making the machine inefficient by kicking the tail from side to side, thus exposing the sides of the fuselage alternately to the air-

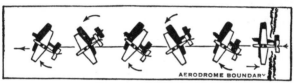

FIG. 19.—Swishtailing.

stream, thereby making them act as a brake. This manœuvre, as in every other in flying, must be done gently. The pilot first puts on rudder. Not only does this make the nose turn, but it also makes the machine bank, because the outside wing is going faster than the inside, and therefore obtaining more lift. To prevent the machine banking, opposite stick must be applied. After a few seconds controls should be centralised, and the same thing done in the opposite direction. This will ensure your not having a blind spot, and you will be able to be quite certain that the way ahead is clear. Great care must be taken that the machine is flying normally when the point of stall is reached, otherwise a severe sideways strain will be imposed upon the under-carriage if the machine touches down crabwise.

A refinement of side-slipping is when it is done while on a turn. Frequently it is convenient to slip off height whilst turning in to the aerodrome. All that the pilot has to do is to put on more bank than is actually necessary for his actual rate of turn, and the machine will slip in. To do this he must keep plenty of speed, and not do it too close to the ground. A slight misjudgment, and he might slip into the ground.

In rough-weather conditions gliding in to land must be done at a faster speed. Instead of gliding in at 60 miles an hour, you must fly at 75. This is so that you will have plenty of control when encountering sudden lulls near the ground or rough forces on either wing which necessitate plenty of control to combat them.

The technique of actual landing is different in rough weather, too. Instead of doing a three-point landing, it is advisable to do a deliberate wheel-landing, taking real care not to allow the machine to balloon. A wheel-landing is more suitable, as the machine with tail up is more stream-lined than with tail down, and therefore less disturbed by gusts.

If, after landing, you find that the wind is so strong that you are unable to steer the machine on the ground, wait in the cockpit until someone sees your plight and comes to lend a guiding hand on a wing-tip. Sometimes conditions are so bad that a pilot has to judge his landing to touch down exactly where mechanics are waiting to catch him. Any wind above the stalling speed of the aircraft will tend to make it fly when it is standing still on the ground. There is therefore good reason for requiring assistance on the ground.

Before leaving landings, mention must be made of cross-wind landings, which are sometimes necessary when the shape of the landing area in relation to the direction of the wind does not provide sufficient length for an " into-wind " landing (Fig. 20). This is normally an unlikely eventuality, but cross-wind landings are sometimes necessary when landing in a hurry.

If you glide down onto the landing area across wind, you will quite easily see that you are being carried sideways over the ground. The nearer you get to the ground the more apparent this is. In order to counteract this sideways drift, dip the windward wing a little and keep the nose still pointing in the same direction by means of a little top rudder. You are then doing a side-slip into wind. According to the amount of drift you have, so you steepen or reduce the bank you have on, adjusting it so that the slip into wind counteracts the drift and your path over the ground is in the

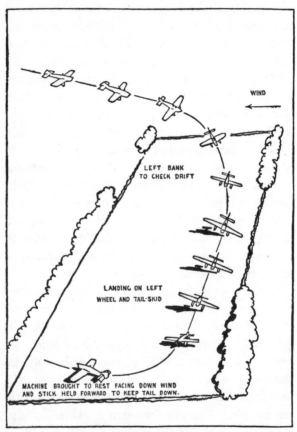

FIG. 20.—A cross-wind landing.

same direction as the nose. Just as you flatten out in order to land, ease the wing-tip up sufficiently to keep it from touching the ground, and land on one wheel and the tail-skid. In this way the machine will make contact with the ground without any sideways drift and imposing no strain on the under-carriage. Keep the machine on one wheel as long as your control will allow it, and then, when it sinks on to the other wheel, turn *down wind* and ease the stick forward so that the wind does not get under the elevators and blow the machine onto its nose. If you turn into wind when there is anything but the lightest of breezes blowing, you are almost certain to be blown onto the outside wing-tip. This is avoided by turning down wind. In carrying out a landing of this nature, it is more important than ever that you have full control, so keep an eye on your A.S.I. and feel your ailerons all the time.

Let me repeat, for safety's sake, whenever you are carrying out a landing, do not blind yourself to everything else that may be happening. Remember that the air around an aerodrome has more aeroplanes in it than anywhere else, so always keep a very good look-out for other machines. For this reason do not get into the habit of always looking over the same side of the cockpit when you are landing. Take frequent glances all around you, and then you will not find yourself in a nasty accident. And remember, too, that there may be obstacles on the ground that do not show up well from the air, so never assume that the landing area is clear for you. If you have any doubt at all as to whether the stretch of ground you have chosen to land on is not entirely clear and suitable (it may, for instance, be boggy), fly over it first, and then approach and land. *And always have plenty of speed.*

Flaps

So many training aircraft are now fitted with flaps that a word on their operation is not out of place.

Flaps are long rectangular surfaces that normally form the trailing edge of the inner section of each wing. But they are hinged so that the pilot, by moving a lever, can depress them any angle up to 90 degrees. In this position they look like two ailerons both depressed 90 degrees.

When depressed, their effect on the flight path of an aircraft gliding down may be twofold. By introducing an exposed surface to the airstream they can perform the function of an air brake with the resultant effect of steepening the glide, and they can give the wing slightly more lift which will have the effect of reducing the landing speed. There are all kinds of flaps with different functions, but these two are the ones that apply to most elementary training aircraft.

They are, of course, of considerable value to a pilot. Modern machines have a very flat guide and it is therefore difficult to judge the point of contact with the ground. Further, if you have to glide over an obstacle, you have to cover a lot of valuable ground before your glide path contacts the aerodrome or field surface. By making his approach with his flaps down, a pilot gives his aircraft a steeper glide which makes his judgment easier, and enables him to contact the ground soon after passing over an obstacle. He can therefore land in a smaller area with his flaps down than he could with them up.

If you make a normal approach with flaps down and then misjudge your landing, open up your engine to full throttle *but do not raise your flaps until you have about 400 feet of height.*

This is most important. The reason is because the action of raising your flaps results in a certain loss of height, so that if you do it too low your aircraft will sink onto the ground.

To sum up: you can always put your flaps down with safety, provided you keep your speed up and do not lower them at a speed above the limit set by the manufacturers (about 100 miles an hour for light aircraft), but once they are down you must not raise them unless you have engine on and plenty of height to spare.

There is one other point you must remember. When you are coming in on a straight approach with flaps down, the change of attitude from a steep glide to flattening out to land is fairly considerable. This results in the wing-loading of the aircraft being increased during the change of attitude, with a consequent increase in the stalling speed. It may rise, for example, from 45 miles an hour to 60 miles an hour if you flatten out with a very " ham " movement of the stick. Bear this always in mind, and avoid trouble by flattening out more gently than you would with flaps up, or, if faced with an emergency, by putting on a little engine at the same time as you start flattening out.

CHAPTER VIII

SPINNING

ONE of the most spectacular aerobatics is the spin. To the lay public this manœuvre is called the spinning nose-dive, and I only mention that term here so that you may be quite sure what this manœuvre looks like. The machine spins around a vertical axis while pointing towards the ground (Fig. 21).

But although it is one of the most spectacular evolutions in aerobatics, it is, curiously enough, an important feature of a pupil's training long before he starts learning aerobatics. This is because an aeroplane may automatically fall into a spin if the pilot manipulates his controls wrongly when near the point of stall. Generally speaking, an aeroplane will spin if at any moment it stalls when one or more of the controls are in an extreme position. Some aeroplanes are more vicious in this respect than others, and one is relieved to find that more and more types of aeroplanes are now being built which are positively reluctant to go into a spin even when the pilot endeavours to spin. But a pupil must learn to spin in order to be familiar with it at any time, and in order that he may get out of it with a minimum loss of height.

The simplest way to put a machine into a spin is to shut off the engine and ease the nose well up until, at the point of stall, the stick is right back. When this moment is reached, put hard rudder on in whichever direction you wish to spin. The machine will appear to hang still in the air, then its wing-tip will drop, the nose will fall suddenly, and the whole will revolve round and round a vertical axis. Until one is used to it, the sensation of spinning is unpleasant. You see the earth revolving very fast around the nose, the machine makes a swish-swish-swish sound, and you very soon begin to feel giddy. A curious feature about it is that when you first do spins, although you may have done only three complete turns, you will feel that you have done twenty-three.

In order to resume normal flight you check a spin in two stages. First you stop the spinning, and then you come out of the resultant dive. The first stage you achieve by putting on hard opposite rudder, at the same time easing the stick slightly forward. After about half a turn the machine will stop spinning, and you will find yourself in a steep dive. You come out of this by centralising the rudder and gently easing the stick back until normal flight is resumed. The important thing to guard against is with regard to the stick. Do not plunge it forward when you want to come out of the spin. Just ease it gently forward.

I have already said that, generally speaking, an aeroplane will spin if it is allowed to stall when one or more of the controls are in an extreme position. Let us consider when this is likely to happen.

Suppose you are gliding down in a fairly steep turn. If you are flying near the stalling speed (remember the stalling speed in a turn is higher than when flying level, and this is sometimes forgotten), and you put on too much bottom rudder, the nose will drop and the machine will skid outwards. In a fit of mental aberration you might quite well forget the attitude of the plane, and pull the stick back in an endeavour to get the nose up again. If you do this, the controls are all set for a spin.

Suppose you are doing a normal turn with engine on but with none too much speed to spare and you put on too much bottom rudder. The machine will skid outwards, the nose will drop, and you may endeavour to get it up again by pulling back on the stick. Here again, if you do this, the controls are all set for a spin.

Suppose you are doing a steep turn with none too much speed to spare and you put on too much *top* rudder. The stick is already well back (the

FIG. 21.—Into and out of a spin.

ideal position for a spin), and you may find the machine falling into a spin in the opposite direction to the turn.

If you side-slip steeply with the stick too far back and at a speed near the stall, the machine may fall into a spin in the opposite direction to the side-slip.

You must not think, as a result of reading this chapter, that an aeroplane takes every opportunity to spin. It does not; but the spin is always waiting to teach the slovenly airman a lesson. Fly accurately, and you will never get into an unintentional spin. Even fly badly, and you will not get into a spin. But fly very badly, and the spin may prove your passport to a happier land, if you have not been left with enough height to recover. I do not believe in being flippant regarding fatal accidents, but I do believe in calling a spade a spade, and more deaths have been caused by careless pilots getting into a spin from which they could not recover in time than by anything else. Fly accurately and carefully, and you will be quite all right. Even be sure never to have too much rudder on, and you will be all right. But do a lot of practice spinning so as to be prepared for an emergency. I have given spinning a chapter to itself, because it is important.

CHAPTER IX

CROSS-COUNTRY FLYING

YOU are not allowed to fly farther than three miles from your aerodrome until you have passed the tests for, and received, the Air Ministry Private Pilot's " A " Licence. This involves an elementary oral examination, the answers to which you can learn in an afternoon, a simple flying test consisting of five figures of eight and a landing within 50 yards of a mark, and a medical report from your local practitioner. The standard of physical fitness required is nothing to be frightened of for the " A " licence.

As soon as you have got your " A ", then the pleasures of flying really start for you. The exquisite joy of your first cross-country flight on your own can only compare with your first solo for ripe satisfaction. There is something about leaving the earth at one spot and coming down an hour later at another in a totally different environment without the gradual adjustment to one's senses that one experiences in a car that defies description. The most hard-boiled of men cannot fail to get a lilt when he feels his wheels touch for the first time on " foreign " soil. But just in the same way as you can be a good or a bad aerobatic pilot, so you can be a good or a bad cross-country pilot. Only industry and application will make you good. But the trouble is that the delights of flying are such, some of the fruits are so easy to taste, that one is inclined to take the easy way and avoid the parts which need those qualities—industry and application. Only in recognition and acknowledgment of them, tempered with earnest concentration, does there lie efficiency and—as far as flying is concerned—*safety*.

The two most important adjuncts to cross-country flying are a compass and a map. The two you use in conjunction. Without a map the compass loses ninety per cent. of its value, and without a compass a map loses about forty per cent. of its value. Let us fly from *A* to *B* and see what has to be done in order to be sure of finding the way.

First you draw a line connecting *A* to *B* on your map. A good map for Great Britain is the Ordnance Survey map with a scale of 4 miles to the inch. You measure off from this line the distance and the course. The distance, let us say, is 100 miles, and the course due North. Now we have already reached a snag. Although the course measured on the map is due North, we have to make an adjustment, because the magnetic compass points to what is known as the Magnetic North, which alters a little every year, but just now is about 12 degrees west of True North. The course to set on the compass is therefore 12 degrees to the East of North. Examine the features marked on the map over which your line is drawn. See what are the main landmarks. There will be a town here and a clearly defined wood there; or the railway line crosses your course twice, and a big river sprawls across too. Note just how far these various landmarks are from your starting-point, and convert the distance into the time it will take you to reach them.

If, for instance, there is no wind and the first big landmark is a town 20 miles away, at a cruising speed of 100 miles an hour over the ground you will reach this town in 12 minutes. On a perfectly clear day this calculation may not be necessary, but on a foggy day it is a great help to know, by the time taken, just how far along your course you are, so that you may be prepared to look out for landmarks. If the visibility is only a mile, and you are travelling at nearly 2 miles a minute, there is none too much time to check your position by fitting the mental picture you have made of some combination of features

beneath you to the pattern of the map. Knowledge of your distance travelled by calculating it
from time taken and speed of machine is also of
inestimable value when you are expecting to
come across a landmark (perhaps it is a railway line crossing your course) and you fail to
find it. If you do not see it, the only way of
knowing your approximate position (and therefore if you have passed it without seeing it) is by
your watch.

Almost invariably there is some sort of wind
blowing—wind which at heights is blowing from
a different direction and with a different speed
from what it is on the ground. It is therefore
necessary on a cross-country flight to allow for
wind direction and speed when you are working
out on what course to fly. This information can
be got roughly from the Meteorological Office, and
with the aid of a Course and Distance Calculator
can be applied to the true course (course over the
ground) between A and B in order to find the
course to steer. I do not propose to describe this
Calculator or how it works, for the simple reason
that I have never yet found it necessary except
when racing. Far better to dispense with instruments that can easily be lost, and find your course
to steer by common sense.

After very few cross-country flights you will

begin to get an idea of the number of degrees into
wind to steer when you are flying a course across
wind or its variants. Suppose on the day you
fly this journey from *A* to *B* there is an easterly
wind of 20 miles an hour; that means that, in
order to allow for it and steer a course over the
ground of 12 degrees East of North, you will have
to steer a course in the air a little more to the East
—about 12 degrees. Set your compass, then, to
24 degrees. After taking off, fly round and over
the aerodrome at the height you are going to fly
the journey at, and, when over the centre of the
aerodrome, settle on your course by compass.
You can turn an ordinary banked turn on to the
rough course, but make final adjustment by means
of a flat turn. The reason for this is that a
compass does not show a banked turn, but it will
fairly accurately show a flat turn. In this connection it is important to say that if ever you find
the compass going a little hay-wire, settle down
on a steady course, and it will soon get steady.
Then you can turn on to your required course.
There is a lot for the professional airman to learn
about a compass, but I do not propose to go into it
in detail here.

Having settled on the course that you estimated
would take you direct from *A* to *B* allowing for
drift (wind), keep on it until you fly above a

landmark marked on your map. If this landmark is shown on the map to have your pencil line

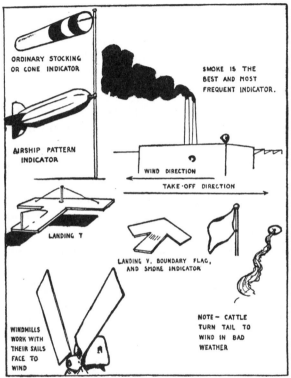

FIG. 22.—When flying across-country, an experienced pilot keeps a constant watch upon the many possible indications of local wind direction.

through it, well and good. You made your calculation for drift correctly. But if you find that it is to the West of your course, then you must make more allowance for wind, so add on another 2 degrees to your compass course, and steer 26 degrees instead of 24 degrees. But before you settle down on the new course, fly direct to a point on your desired course, and then turn on to the new one and repeat the procedure to find out if you have estimated correctly. By this method of trial and error you can very soon find the course to steer, and you are independent of everything but your common sense and experience. With a little of the latter in your bag, you will have no difficulty in finding your course within five minutes of leaving the aerodrome.

Once you know the course to steer, the essential thing is to trust your compass. On occasions you will find, especially in bad weather, that when an expected landmark does not turn up, you will think that you are steering too much this way or that, or even that your compass has taken into its head to go wrong. On such occasions keep your head and trust your compass. It will not have gone wrong. Calculate by time taken from the last recognised landmark just how far from it you are, and lay this distance along the line on your map. You will be mighty near that point although you can gain no recognition from the earth that speeds swiftly by below you.

When, by your time calculation you are quite sure you have passed it, if it is a good mark like a railway line, it may be a good idea to turn back on the *reciprocal course* (reverse course) and look again.   Or, if you come across a railway line and you are lost, fly along it until it leads you to a well-defined town or junction which you will be able to recognise from your map, bearing in mind your rough location.

You should not really set off on a cross-country flight before you have become reasonably proficient at forced landings.   These you can practise assiduously in the vicinity of your aerodrome. Although forced landings are fortunately rare nowadays, engines do still fail on occasions, and it is as well to be equipped to deal with such sudden emergency.   Anyone can soon learn to fly an aeroplane, but much practice and patience are required before you can be competent to deal with emergencies, so do not be satisfied with your flying until you *are* competent to deal with emergencies.

At the risk of appearing immodest, let me give an example of what I mean.   In the summer of 1938 I was flying a 200-mile-an-hour machine with three passengers on board.   The engine was of as reliable a make as you can get anywhere, and a stoppage was the last thing I expected.   The aerodrome to which I was going was already in sight when suddenly there was an ugly metallic thumping noise, the engine stopped—and then burst into flames.

The cabin filled with smoke, and we had to open the windows to get some air. Whether this had any salutary effect I do not know. I was flying 600 feet up at 170 miles an hour over hilly country. Just ahead of me, and below, I spotted the only possible place where I could land—a small green field on the side of a steep hill. If I landed *up* the hill, I would need only a fraction of the space to pull up in that this fast aeroplane normally needed. I was conscious that it was essential that we did not have even a minor crash, for that would mean a breakage in the fuel system and we would go up " whoof " before we had a chance to escape.

I side-slipped violently to lose both height and speed in the shortest possible time, and landed successfully. Now, then : I am perfectly certain that I would have failed to pull off that landing had I not been in the habit of making every single landing on an aerodrome I had ever made in my flying career a make-believe forced landing. I have never been content just to get into an aerodrome. I have always chosen a mark on its surface and landed as near to it (without the aid of engine, and therefore like a forced landing) as I possibly could. After some thousands of those "forced landings" I had equipped myself to get out of the unusual and nasty situation with which I was faced that day.

Take my tip, and do the same. Treat every landing as a forced landing, and triumph at the moment of trial is, believe me, worth all the trouble and patience of preparation for it.

There are two main difficulties about a forced landing. The first is the ability to choose a suitable place in which to land, and the second is the ability to judge your approach accurately without the use of an engine to get you out of a difficulty.

Curiously enough, although you might not think it, the first of these difficulties is the one that gives most trouble. You can practise forced landings at your home aerodrome until you have attained a high standard of judgment, but it is very much harder to gain practice in recognising suitable landing-surfaces from the air. The only way to do this is to do dummy forced landings when you are on a cross-country flight. Approach onto a likely field and open up the engine just before you touch down. After you have done a few of these, the awful truth will be borne upon you that fields are not as flat as they look from the air, nor are they necessarily as smooth as they look. But when you are doing these dummy approaches take care you do not do them anywhere near livestock. Unfortunately, careless pilots have done tremendous damage to livestock by frightening them at critical periods of their lives. Even healthy young horses have been known to be impaled in a mad endeavour to jump an impossible fence in order to flee from the terror in the sky.

The first thing you must do when your engine suddenly stops is to ease the stick forward. Especially is this important if you are climbing. Immediately the power goes, ease forward the stick and get into a glide, otherwise you will naturally stall. At the same time look over the side and give a quick glance at all the ground within gliding distance. Then eliminate the areas that are definitely too small for you to land in. In this connection it is a good idea, when you are on your cross-country flights, to get into the habit of choosing fields in which to land supposing your engine failed at any moment. After a time you will do this unconsciously, and at the moment of trial will be familiar with the ground beneath you.

Always choose a grass field in which to land if there is a suitable one, but do not take for granted that it is smooth. If you look closely at it you may see that it has furrows. In which case it may be all right for you if you land along the furrows.   This may involve a cross-wind landing which is quite feasible provided the wind is not too strong or, if it is strong, if the direction of the furrows is not too much across it.   When estimating in your mind whether a field is big enough to land in, remember that the final approach is an important factor.   If it is bordered by a high fence, houses, or trees, then you will not be able to touch down in the field until some distance from its boundary

As soon as you have selected your field, have a look round inside the cockpit to see if you can ascertain the cause of the engine failure.   You may perhaps have caught the switches when you were unfolding a map, or perhaps the petrol-cock has inadvertently been turned off.   This is not so unlikely as it sounds.   I was once flying a machine on the outside of a formation when our leader decided to do a fast spiral dive to get under a layer of cloud.   Being on the outside of the turn in a large formation of powerful machines I had to go extremely fast, with the engine over-revving. Suddenly it stopped, and I was faced with a forced landing at low height and in bad weather. I looked automatically at the switches, then the petrol-cock.   I saw the cock at the " off " position.   The vibration had turned it off.   I quickly turned it on, the engine spluttered and then picked

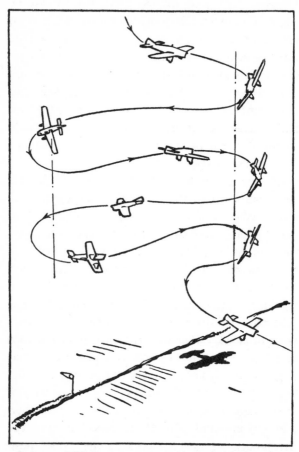

FIG. 23.—" S " turns as a means of losing height for a forced landing approach. Turns should be made 200 yards from boundary.

up, and the situation was saved purely by my automatic action of looking at cock and switches.

The best procedure for the approach is to glide as soon as possible to the leeward side of the selected field and then lose height by gliding parallel to it, so that you can turn in immediately you are at the correct height to touch down in the field.   If you have much height to lose, then come down in a series of " S " turns (Fig. 23), gliding first in one direction, then in the other, but always parallel to the leeward boundary, and about 200 yards from it.   Do your turns towards the field (into wind), and guard against the tendency to get nearer and nearer to it.   Judge the approach so that you touch down about a third of the way up the field ;   you can always side-slip away surplus height at the last moment ;   but you cannot gain height without your engine.   Always, then, have too much height rather than too little.   You will not hurt yourself if you run into the far hedge at the end of your landing run, but you *will* hurt yourself if you hit the leeward hedge when you are going at flying speed.

The great thing to remember is, once you have selected your field, stick to it.   Do not change at the last minute.   Almost certainly it will look much more unsatisfactory than you supposed when you were higher up, but never mind.   Do not confuse your judgment by last-minute changes. For this same reason, when you have made certain that the engine has definitely failed, close the throttle, and keep it closed.   Otherwise it may give a temporary burst just as you are about to land and leave you in a really bad position by failing again at no height and with nowhere suitable to land.   Keep a very good look-out for telephone-wires and power-cables.   These have a nasty habit of remaining invisible.

It is important to learn the characteristics of the chief types of land which are liable to be met with by a pilot faced with a forced landing.   The following descriptions I take, with acknowledgements, from the R.A.F. *Flying Training Manual*. They give a better picture than I can hope to portray.

" *Grass* appears a dull uniform green or, in autumn, a brownish-green colour   It may often be recognised by the presence of horses, cattle or sheep grazing on it.

" *Stubble* appears buff coloured in the autumn, according to the time which has elapsed since the crop has been cut.   In stubble regular rows can generally be seen.   Stubble is one of the best surfaces for landing on.

" *Growing crops*.—The colour of these varies according to the seasons, but is much brighter in spring and lighter in colour than grass or stubble. They can be recognised by their regular appearance and by the spaces generally found between rows. Crops should be avoided, especially in summer. In a strong wind, high crops and long grass show ripples or waves as the wind passes through them.

" *Root crops* appear dark green from the air with regular rows. Root-crops make a bad landing-ground, but may be used as such in an emergency if an aircraft is landed slowly parallel to the rows or furrows of the crop, provided that the velocity and direction of the wind allow.

" *Ploughed land* is more general in late autumn and winter, and has a rich brown or red colour which varies according to the soil of the district. Ploughed land makes bad landing-ground except in very dry or frosty weather.

" *Sand* appears very light yellow or almost white when dry, and varies greatly in its suitability as a landing-ground. Dry, shifting sand is generally too soft for landing, but sand that is moist and firm is suitable. On a beach the sand a few yards from the water's edge is generally suitable.

" *Snow* is very uncertain, and possesses the disadvantage of concealing the surface and of rendering obstacles invisible. The pilot should scan the surface for shadows which may indicate

E

an obstacle or a depression in the ground, and should endeavour to execute a very slow landing.

" *Water*.—A normal landing should be made as near to the shore as practicable. The aircraft should be held off a little higher than normal, so that the alighting is made as slowly as possible and with the tail well down. The pilot must pancake from a sufficient height to ensure alighting on the water with practically no forward speed and as near to the shore as possible."

CHAPTER X

AEROBATICS

THERE are those who think that aerobatics are nothing more than evolutions to be indulged in by young pilots anxious to show off to their friends below. This idea has been gained because of the fact that too often a pilot has been killed by doing aerobatics badly and too low, and the newspapers, printing a report of the coroner's inquest, have told how the deceased pilot had flown over from —— aerodrome and was stunting above the house of a friend. The reading public therefore jumps to the conclusion that the only time a pilot does do aerobatics is when he is trying to show off, and that inevitably they are a dangerous form of entertainment.

The fact is, that apart from the obvious application of aerobatics to air fighting by the military pilot, experience of them is a great asset to the ordinary pilot. They are a means of providing him with confidence in himself and his machine. By deliberately putting his machine into an unusual manœuvre and knowing how to come out of it, he is likely to be able to cope with that emergency which may come once in a lifetime when, from some set of circumstance, he finds himself in a frightening attitude in a storm very close to the ground. Familiarity in aerobatics makes a pilot free from the terrors that might beset him on such an occasion and capable of safely recovering from the situation. Aerobatics are also bound to give a pilot confidence in his machine. Obviously some machines are not meant to be aerobated, and the fact that a pilot cannot aerobat them does not mean that he will lack confidence in them. But experience of aerobating other machines will give him confident knowledge of the capabilities and strength of modern aeroplanes.

The golden rule is, of course, not to aerobat low down. An airman's vanity is a most curious thing. If he is young and gay and the world feels good to him and he is flying along on a cross-country flight on a bright, sunny day and, looking over the side of his cockpit, he spies a small crowd of people on the earth far beneath him looking at a village football match, he will feel an itch to dive down and stunt above them. He will not know a soul among them; they will not have the slightest idea who he is. An ordinary direct charge of vanity cannot therefore be preferred against this airman. His urge to show off is cloaked by an impenetrable veil of anonymity. His audience does not know him from Adam; he knows none of his audience. Yet still that urge to stunt before them will be there—if he is young and gay and the world feels good to him. But if he has reached the flying age of discretion, he will resist the impulse, and he will realise that for every one of his audience who looks at his stunting plane in gaping interest, there will be a hundred who are trying to read his registration letters to report him to the police.

Low stunting must only be carried out by pilots engaged at flying meetings to give exhibitions. These are always experienced men well versed in the art of aerobatics and acutely conscious of the limitations within which a pilot must work in order to aerobat in safety. The spectators, too, can be counted on as being favourable towards the exhibitions, because presumably they would not be there if they were going to complain about the noise and thrill of low flying.

Roughly speaking, aerobatics can be divided into two classes: those that do not involve inverted flying, and those that do. By inverted flying I mean flying which for varying periods involves the machine actually flying inverted. Looping, although the machine is upside-down at the top of a loop, does not involve inverted flying. At no time during a loop is the weight of the machine borne by the *top* surface of the wing.   In inverted flying the weight of the machine is borne by the top surface of the wing.

There are other manœuvres, such as the barrel roll and flick roll, during which the machine is upside down momentarily, but which do not involve inverted flying.

For none of the aerobatics which come under this classification is any special equipment necessary for pilot or engine.   Indeed, a skilled aerobatic pilot can give a most comprehensive and thrilling display of aerobatics, during which his machine is frequently upside-down, without his even being held into his seat by a belt.   As a precaution he would certainly be properly strapped in, but if he did his aerobatics accurately and well, his weight need never be taken off his seat, and therefore there would be no tendency for him to fall out.

The second type of aerobatics—those that involve inverted flying—necessitate the pilot being strapped in by a special harness, generally a " Sutton " harness.   This is a system of four straps which hold him firmly to his seat inverted or right way up.   When the machine is inverted, the pilot's weight is taken up by the two straps which are led over his shoulders. All four straps of the " Sutton " harness meet at and are fixed by a pin which comes approximately over the pilot's stomach. This pin is so designed that with one pull the pilot can instantly free himself from the straps, an important factor in an emergency, when he may want to quit the machine by parachute or get clear of wreckage after a crash. Every split second is vital on such occasions.

The Loop

The easiest evolution to do is, strangely enough, the loop (Fig. 25). I say " strangely enough " because ever since it was first done by a brave Frenchman before the war, this manœuvre has kept the public's fancy as the acme of aerobatics. To the layman the loop still represents the epitome of a pilot's skill and bravery. How reluctant one is, therefore, to have to admit that the loop is one of the easiest manœuvres in flying !

Before doing a loop, it is necessary to gain a little extra speed, so, after looking around you to see that there are no other aircraft in the vicinity, ease the nose down a little and give the engine three-quarter throttle. Observe and note some spot on the horizon on which you must come out of the loop, so that you may be sure

Fig. 24.—The pilot's view from the top of a loop.

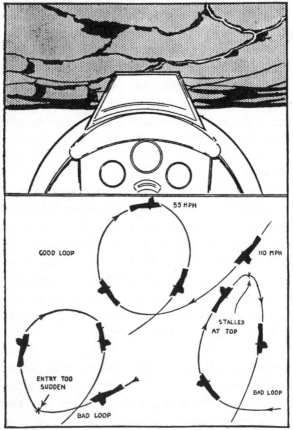

Fig. 25.—The loop.

of doing a straight one and finishing in exactly the same direction to that in which you started. When you have reached a speed of about 120 miles an hour, start easing back the stick, at the same time pushing the throttle full open so that the engine gives all its power. You want to ease the stick back gently but firmly. As you are going fast, you will find it stiff, and you will also find that the comparatively sudden change of direction to which you are subjecting the machine results in a strong application of centrifugal force which presses you hard down on your seat. It is, however, by the feel of this force that you can determine the strain to which you are subjecting the machine. Experience will tell you just to what degree the stick should be eased back. As the machine mounts up and over, it obviously loses speed rapidly, and this in turn reduces the effect of the controls. As you go up, therefore, so you want to continue easing back your stick, until, when you are upside-down at the top of the loop, the stick is as far back in your stomach as it can go. At this point shut off the throttle (the engine will stop anyhow when it is upside-down) and keep the stick back until the nose drops and the speed increases again. Then ease the stick forward as necessary to come out of the resultant dive. When you are once again

E 2

flying level, then you can open up the engine again.

It is easy to do a sloppy loop, but, like everything else in flying, much practice and concentration are required before you can do a neat one : one that is perfectly smooth to the onlooker, with no " corners ", and which does not suffer from a crooked path or dipped wing at the top of the loop. In fact, the rudder plays as important a part in the loop as the elevator.

If you do not judge a loop properly, one of two things may happen. By pulling back on the stick roughly and too quickly you will strain the machine, besides making it extremely uncomfortable for yourself, and if you are too timid and do not ease back on the stick enough, you will " hang " on top of the loop and stall when inverted. You have to judge it so that you maintain flying speed all the time. Obviously, if you take too long over the steep climb on the first half of the loop, you will lose flying speed. If you are upside-down when you do this, you will leave your seat, because it is centrifugal force which keeps you in, and that depends on the rate of change of direction. You can swing a bucket full of water around your head without spilling a drop so long as you swing it fast enough ; but if you swing it too slowly, all the water will fall out as soon as the bucket is inverted. Exactly the same thing happens in a looping aeroplane.

Provided you are properly strapped in, you need not fear the consequences of hanging on top of a loop. The worst that can happen is for the machine to fall into an ordinary spin, and you can easily get out of that. What you must avoid is too *tight* a loop, which is rank bad piloting and, as already explained, strains the machine. Instead of flying cleanly round, the machine " squashes " the air and loses considerable speed.

Stall Turn

A stall turn is an easy manœuvre to do and graceful to watch (Fig. 26). Fly along level, and ease the nose up until it is pointing vertically into the air. Having gained this position, shut the throttle. The machine will almost immediately stall; but just before it does, put on hard rudder one way or the other, in whichever direction you wish to do the turn. The sensation is a curious one—a sort of complete suspension and stillness— and then suddenly the nose drops and the machine gets into a dive from which you recover in the ordinary way. You take off the rudder, of course, as soon as flying speed is regained in the dive.

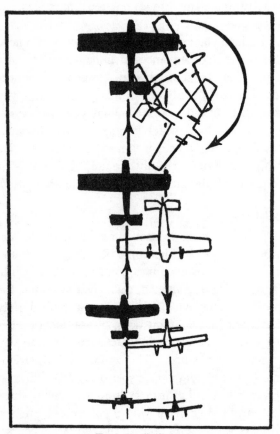

FIG. 26.—Stall turn.

Immelman Turn

An Immelman is one of the most graceful manœuvres in all flying (Fig. 27). Apart from that, it has the severely practical advantage of being the quickest way of making a " right-about " turn.

Fly along level, and then put the machine into

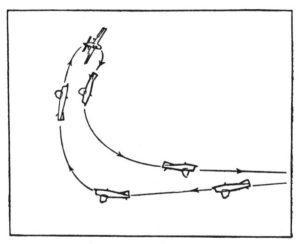

FIG. 27.—Immelman turn.

a steep climbing turn—steep both in climb and bank. Hold the climb until the machine is in a vertical bank, with its speed (because of the gain in height) considerably reduced. Then go straight into a diving turn, gradually taking off your bank and reducing the rate of turn as you approach the desired direction. The manœuvre is completed when the machine is at the same height and flying in the opposite direction to that which it was before.

For display purposes it is impressive to do an exaggerated Immelman, by which I mean a turn of more than 180 degrees—of 270 degrees, for example. In such a turn, although starting to the left, you come out at right angles to the right of your original direction. To do such a turn you start in the normal Immelman way, but instead of being in a steep bank at the top of the turn, you keep the stick over until you are actually on your back, so judging it that you finish the resultant dive having completed a turn of 270 degrees. You fly round this turn all the time, in the same way that you fly round in a loop. At no time is the machine flying inverted, although at one moment it is upside-down. Throughout an Immelman turn rudder must be adjusted to bank so that the machine does not skid or slip.

Flick Roll

There is little to commend this evolution. It is ugly to watch, uncomfortable to do, and not good for the machine. It is, unfortunately, easy to do, and is therefore one of the first manœuvres that a pilot keen on aerobatics wishes to try. Although ugly to watch, it is somewhat spectacular.

A flick roll is really nothing more than a horizontal spin in which one complete roll is made— a roll in this case being the equivalent of a turn in a spin. To do this unpleasant evolution, fly along level at a speed slightly less than cruising speed. Then pull back the stick, at the same time putting on full rudder in whichever direction you wish to roll—and ugh! the thing is done. You can readily appreciate the strain to which the machine is put. As soon as the full roll is completed you ease the stick forward and apply opposite rudder. If you do not do this soon enough, you will get into a spin.

Flick Half-Roll

This is much better and, to the bargain, has a useful function. As its name implies, a flick half-roll is the first half of a flick roll, and is a useful manœuvre by which to change direction prior to starting a dive. Fly level at a little over stalling speed, ease back the control column and apply full rudder in the required direction. The machine will immediately flick over on to its back, when you apply opposite rudder. You keep the stick back until the machine starts its dive, then you ease the stick forward and at the same time centralise the rudder.

Falling Leaf

This manœuvre is so named because the air-craft has the appearance of a leaf falling from a tree and fluttering from side to side (Fig. 28). Though not strictly accurate, the manœuvre can be described as a series of alternate side-slips just above the point of stall.

Fly level just above the point of stall and with a little engine on. This will assist you to keep control during this difficult evolution. Put the stick hard over to one side, at the same time easing it a little back. The wing dropping, the nose will drop, so prevent this by putting on hard opposite rudder. Then immediately put the stick hard over in the opposite direction, again slightly back, at the same time applying opposite rudder. Continue to do this alternately, and the machine will swish from side to side out of a bank on one side into a bank on the other. When you want to resume normal flight, centralise the control and put on engine.

Because the machine is at the point of stall, this manœuvre is extremely difficult to do neatly. Particularly hard is it to keep it pointing in the same direction all the time. From a spectator's

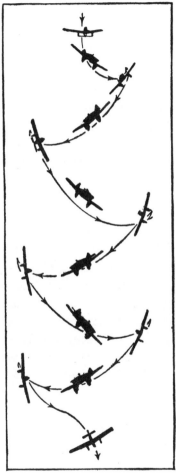

FIG. 28.—Falling leaf.

point of view it is best to do it into wind.   The
" falling leaf " will then appear to be losing height
nearly vertically.

We now come on to a few evolutions which
involve inverted flying. Unless an engine is
especially fitted so that it will run when inverted,
the pilot's repertoire is somewhat restricted.   But
he can fly inverted all right by maintaining speed
by gliding inverted or by having surplus speed
sufficient to carry out whatever manœuvre he
may wish to do inverted.

Inverted Flying

Unless you are properly strapped in with
shoulder-straps, you will not be in the plane any
longer than your first attempt at one evolution.
So do not try them unless you are strapped in
tightly.   If, later on, you take a passenger on an
aerobatic flight, see that he is strapped in *tightly*
too, especially if the machine is fitted with dual
controls.   I nearly came to grief once by not
seeing for myself that my passenger had his
shoulder-straps tight on an instructional flight in
aerobatics.   While we were inverted, his packed
parachute slipped from under him and forward in
such a way that, try as I would, I could not get
my stick back enough to recover from a dive from
the inverted position.   The plane just levelled out

before we reached the ground, but with only a few feet to spare. Never, therefore, take for granted that your passenger knows how to strap himself in. See for yourself that his straps are tight and properly done up.

Help your engine by throttling back as soon as you are inverted. It will stop anyway, but it will not be strained by starting again with the throttle fully forward when level flight is regained.

Before trying to do any aerobatics that involve inverted flying, it is necessary to become accustomed to the peculiar sensation of such flying. There are many ways of turning a machine on its back, the easiest being by doing the first half of a loop and then, when the machine is upsidedown, easing forward the stick. If you keep the nose slightly below the horizon, you will in this way do an inverted glide.

The first surprise that you will get when you are on your back is the unexpected weight of your legs. Unless your feet are through loops on the rudder bar, your legs will heavily drop to the top of the cockpit (the top being on the bottom when inverted !). You can avoid this happening either by having loops on each arm of the rudderbar through which you put your feet, or by pressing slightly on the rudder-bar so that you crook your heel around it.

You will also experience a nasty feeling that, in spite of your shoulder-straps, you are going to fall out, and probably you will try to hang on to the seat with your hands. The reason for this is that however tight you have adjusted your straps, your weight is bound to be transferred from your postérieur to your shoulders, and so you feel as though you are leaving your seat. The tighter your straps the less this uncomfortable feeling asserts itself. But you need not worry about it. Your straps *will* hold your weight many times over, and it only remains for you to trust to your straps and relax.

Against these unpleasant surprises is the pleasant one that you will not feel physically uncomfortable because of your blood allegedly rushing to your head. Unless you remain inverted for a minute or more, you will not suffer the slightest ill effect from this direction.

An aeroplane is designed to be stable when flying the right way up. It follows, therefore, that when it is inverted, this stability is very much reduced. It therefore has to be " flown " all the time. It will not automatically correct small displacements. Further, the controls are designed for maximum effect when flying the right way up, so that when inverted they do not have the effect to the same extent as when in the normal flying position. In order to make corrections or gain a desired effect, the pilot has to be coarser in his movement of the controls. This will be immediately apparent when you ease the stick forward at the top of the loop to start an inverted glide. There is a strong tendency for the nose to drop, and to prevent this you must hold the stick firmly forward.

The simplest way to get off your back and resume normal flight is by easing the stick back and completing the second half of a loop. But this method involves not only loss of height, but also change of direction. The more usual way is to roll off.

Slow Roll and Half-Roll

The slow roll involves the complete rotation of the machine around its longitudinal axis (Fig. 29). In actual practice it is not possible literally to rotate it around this axis, but the pilot should try to do so as near as possible. It is a useful manœuvre to practise, because it is necessary for the pilot to have a high degree of accuracy in the changing functions of the controls in various attitudes of flight.

I have already referred to the machine being nose-heavy when inverted and the consequent effort of the pilot that is required to keep the stick forward. This effort can be reduced in the usual way by putting the tail-trim forward. Before doing aerobatics that involve a lot of inverted flying it is therefore wise to set the tail-trim slightly forward—not too much, or else it will be tiring to hold the stick back in when flying right way up.

When about to do a slow roll, the first thing is

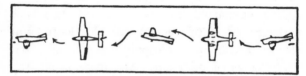

FIG. 29.—Slow roll.

to settle on a point of the horizon on which to steer. Synchronisation of the controls throughout the roll must be such that the aircraft remains pointing on to that same point of the horizon. Nothing looks worse, or more betrays slovenly flying, than a roll which is crooked.

Having chosen your point (by the way, a roll always looks neater from the ground if it is done into wind), ease the nose down to gain a little speed. 110 miles an hour is enough. Then ease back on the stick until the nose is above the horizon, and at the same time, if you are rolling to the right, ease the stick over to the right-hand side of the cockpit. This must be done firmly, because the ailerons will offer a fair amount of resistance at this speed. The machine will then immediately start to bank to the right. Adjust the rudder so that it remains straight. As soon as a fair amount of bank has been put on, the nose will start to drop. This must be counteracted by top rudder. When the machine is vertically on its side, the elevator becomes entirely responsible for keeping it straight (as in a vertically banked turn). The stick has therefore to be eased forward to prevent the machine turning to the right; at the same time it is kept in the right side of the cockpit in order to continue the roll. As the machine gets on to its back, shut off the throttle and keep the stick forward in order to keep the nose above the horizon. This forward stick is gradually taken off as the machine rolls off its back, and again top rudder has to be applied to keep the nose just above the horizon. As you get past the vertical position, take off the rudder as necessary and ease forward the throttle, so judging it that the controls are once again centralised and the engine is running normally at the moment of resuming level flight. It is easy to get into the habit of rolling one way only. Do not allow this to happen. Give yourself equal opportunity to roll to the left.

A half-roll, as its name succinctly implies, is—
half of a roll (Fig. 30). It is a way of either starting a dive or of changing direction. A flick half-roll
also achieves both these objects, but differs from

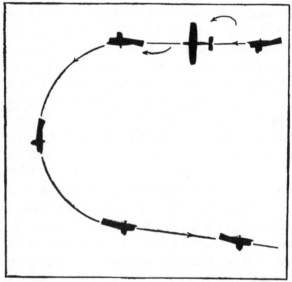

FIG. 30.—Half-roll.

the half-roll in the fact that the machine is near
the point of stall. In an ordinary half-roll it has
full flying speed. This may or may not be an
advantage, according to circumstances. It must
be realised, however, that, as the machine is flying at normal speed at the commencement of a

half-roll, it will have a comparatively high speed in the dive which forms the second part of the half-roll manœuvre, and it will therefore lose more height than the dive resulting from a flick half-roll.

This speed can be checked a little either by starting the manœuvre at slow speed (the machine has to have full flying speed) or with the nose high above the horizon. The manœuvre is done as a combination of the first half of a slow roll and the second half of a loop. When in the inverted position, close the throttle, so that excessive speed is not gained in the dive, which is similar to the second half of a loop.

Half-Roll off the Top of a Loop

This manœuvre is a useful one for changing direction, at the same time gaining height. Its name is self-explanatory—the first half of a loop followed by the second half of a slow roll (Fig. 31).

In order that ample flying speed is in hand at the top of the loop which will enable the controls to operate successfully, it is necessary to start this manœuvre with more speed than is necessary for a loop. Ease the nose well down and get up to a speed of about 130 miles an hour. Then gently ease the stick back as though you were going to execute a loop. When the machine is

on its back, ease the stick forward so as to prevent the nose dropping, at the same time ease
the stick to whichever side you are going to roll
off. As usual, the nose must be kept straight
with a combination of rudder and elevator.

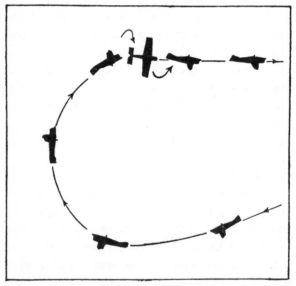

FIG. 31.—Half-roll off the top of a loop.

A good point to remember when executing this
manœuvre is to counteract the tendency of the
machine to have insufficient speed to half-roll off
neatly by waiting until the nose is well below the
horizon before you start to roll off.

Upward Roll

An upward roll is simply a roll which is performed while the machine is climbing. A large amount of extra speed is required to do this manœuvre unless your engine is fitted so as to fly inverted.

Bunt

A bunt is an outside loop, and is not a manœuvre to be recommended to any but the experienced pilot in a machine specially designed for advanced aerobatics, as it imposes a great strain on the machine. The pilot being on the outside of the loop instead of the inside, there is centrifugal force trying to throw him out of the cockpit all the time. Again, unless the machine is fitted with an engine that will run when inverted, it will be impossible for the pilot to complete the second half of the bunt.

To wind up this chapter on aerobatics, I am going to quote from an article written by Herr Rudolph Lochner, who was champion aerobatic pilot of Germany and the Netherlands for 1937. I am indebted to Shell Aviation News for permission to reproduce Herr Lochner's interesting views :—

" The idea that aerobatics are beyond the capabilities of the ordinary pilot is a misconception based on the fact that only the expert does them in public. They should be just as much a part of the training of a pilot as the more simple manœuvres, for they are fundamentally the same thing.

" Aerobatics begin with a perfectly flown circuit of the aerodrome. Whenever I make this statement it always astonishes my listeners, and even good pilots are inclined to assume that it is intended as a joke; and yet it is immensely difficult to fly even one circuit round the aerodrome faultlessly, and even more so to do a second exactly the same as the first. It requires continuous and diligent practice; allowance has to be made for wind and air conditions and height, direction, and speed have to be observed most accurately. The turns must always be made at the same place, and, in addition, there must be the same rate of change of direction with the same degree of bank; and at the conclusion the landing is made in the same way, a feat which is very near to the impossible. The demands made on the pilot in performing this evolution show how close a manœuvre calling for precision is to one calling for special capabilities. That is how a circuit of the aerodrome becomes the first step in aerobatics.

" I have demonstrated how accuracy in flying

is a feature of aerobatics; a further one is the acquisition of perfect control over the aircraft in whatever position it is. While accuracy is a matter for our senses and understanding, this is a matter of mentality. Aerobatics train us to develop the mentality to meet the serious incidents in flying, and are not an end in themselves. In the event of trouble developing in flight, the trained and experienced aerobatic pilot will make the right decision quickly and calmly. He brings his aircraft back from any undesired and unusual flying attitude to the normal in the shortest possible time and with as little strain on it as possible. He is familiar with all attitudes, flying conditions and movements, and knows how to change from one to the other. His aerobatic training enables him to appreciate a situation quickly.

" When he becomes a pilot, a man enters an element which is unfamiliar—he knows land and water, but not air. None of his ancestors have been up in the air, and he lacks the inherited sense which makes things easy for him elsewhere. He lacks the senses of a bird, and is not familiar with air space and the phenomena which he meets there such as sudden changes in altitude and speed. Enormous centrifugal forces, for example, which are not encountered elsewhere, may be encountered for the first time; the whole rhythm of existence in the air is different from that on the ground.

" Sometimes even during a quite ordinary flight something develops which is far from ordinary, and in aerobatic flying this may be, to say the least of it, queer; for the laws of Nature as we know them seem to have been turned topsy-turvy. Normally one falls downwards towards the earth : is it not extraordinary, then, that one should be, under certain conditions, impelled upwards, away from the aircraft and towards the sky ? And then often it is amazingly difficult to stretch an arm or hand downwards in the direction of the earth. Our blood, too, is subject to physical laws, and is affected by the centrifugal and centripetal forces. As it is a very component substance of the human body, these effects are of supreme importance. Our senses can only work as long as they are fed by the blood, and in aerobatic flying shortage or excess may occur in any of our various organs, depending on the course the aerobatic figures and movements take, and the pressures and forces they involve. Insufficiently supplied with blood, our organs refuse to work; if the blood is kept away from the brain by centrifugal force, we lose our faculty of thinking and our consciousness. Before that stage is reached, however, we lose slowly our faculty for seeing, and this is always the signal for us to allow the blood to return to the brain; this is easily done by a slight movement of the controls, provided the body is well rested and elastic. In the case of great bodily tiredness, which may be caused by too much aerobatics, stronger measures may have to be taken, because the vascular system of the body is then so weak that it can no longer resist. In such cases certain compensation can be made by increasing the quantity of blood fluid, for if the blood-vessels extend, the quantity of blood becomes relatively smaller.

" The advantages of aerobatic training cannot be denied, but they are only to be enjoyed through continual practice and training to overcome the mental and physical difficulties. Here a distinction may be made between practice and training, for by practice we understand the art of learning anything, and by training attaining the appropriate physical, intellectual and mental condition for that purpose. I can master something by practice without having trained for it, but only training makes it possible for me to repeat the procedure at any time equally well. Knowledge and ability are therefore not everything, and training is of paramount importance."

CHAPTER XI

PER ARDUA AD ASTRA

"Never in the field of human conflict was so much owed by so many to so few."

I WRITE this chapter particularly for you fellows in the Air Training Corps, so as to give you an idea of the different jobs that await you in the air. Not all of you can be members of an aircrew, but each of you has a chance to be, and this chapter will give you some idea of what form your training will take if you are selected for aircrew duties.

You will go first to a Receiving Wing to be " kitted up ", and from there you will be sent to an Initial Training Wing. You will not know until the end of your course at the Initial Training Wing whether you will be selected as an air gunner, a wireless operator/air gunner, an air observer or a pilot; but in spite of what you might think to the contrary, you really will be " selected " for one of these duties. There is no question of your having failed to " make the grade " as a potential pilot if you are selected to train as one of the other members of the air crew.

Everyone has a vague idea of the duties of a pilot, but they are not so familiar with the duties of the other members of an air crew.

Air Gunner

Suppose you are selected as an air gunner. You will be primarily responsible for the defence of your aircraft against possible attacks by enemy fighters—obviously a duty of the very highest importance. All your training will be directed towards your efficiency in this respect.

You proceed first to a Bombing and Gunnery School for an intensified course of armament training. During this period you will be given a sound and comprehensive training on the ground and in the air under the close supervision of very experienced instructors.

The syllabus of training embraces all aspects of your duties as an air gunner, and includes lectures on guns : their mechanism and maintenance, power-operated gun-turrets, theory of sighting and gun-sights, and gunnery tactics.

The first part of your time at the Bombing and Gunnery School will be taken up with practical demonstrations on the ground, during which you will be given every opportunity of handling and familiarising yourself with the equipment which you will later use in the air. To simulate

F

conditions in the air at this stage, ingeniously designed synthetic training devices are employed.

Your air training will commence as early as possible after the necessary initial lectures and demonstrations have been given. You will carry out progressive aiming exercises in the air, using cine-camera guns, and you will later carry out air-firing exercises against ground targets, targets towed by another aircraft, and targets towed by the aircraft in which you yourself are actually flying. These exercises are all designed to simulate typical attacks by enemy aircraft.

Throughout your course you will obtain constant practice in the manipulation of power-operated turrets on the ground and in the air, in aircraft recognition, and in range estimation. In addition, you will be given instruction on the various types of ammunition and their uses, and on certain pyrotechnics, which an air gunner may be called upon to use during operational flights. All through the course time is devoted to physical training and organised games, since it is most essential that you shall achieve a high degree of physical fitness and endurance in order to be able to withstand the physical and physiological strain imposed by operational flying. You may possibly be one of those who do not take easily to physical jerks, but it is absolutely essential for you to reach and maintain as high a standard as possible of physical fitness all the time you are on operational work. Remember your great responsibilities with regard to the other members of the crew of the aircraft, and the effort will be easy to make.

On passing out satisfactorily from the Bombing and Gunnery School you will be awarded the coveted air gunner's brevet, and will be granted the temporary rank of sergeant. Under normal conditions you will then be posted to an Operational Training Unit, where you will undergo further detailed and specialised instruction applicable to the type of aircraft in which you will actually fly on operations. On the conclusion of this course you will be ready and confident to take your place in an operational squadron.

Wireless Operator/Air Gunner

It may be that you will be selected to become a wireless operator/air gunner, in which case you will be trained as a wireless operator before proceeding to a Bombing and Gunnery School to be trained as an air gunner.

This wireless-operator course is divided into two parts.

During the first part nearly one-half of your total instruction at the Electrical and Wireless

School is devoted to signalling, and it is, of course, essential that you acquire an intimate knowledge of morse code and signalling procedure.

Quite as important as a high standard of morse is an accurate knowledge of procedure, *i.e.*, the use of preliminary calls, answers and operating signals, requesting and giving repetitions, cancelling and resumption of a message, degrees of priority and simple R/T procedure (" R/T " is speaking transmission and " W/T " is morse transmission).

Concurrent with this training you will be lectured on science and English, as it is necessary for you to understand the underlying principles of electricity and to be able to write quickly, spell accurately and do simple arithmetical calculations with ease. The syllabus covers a grounding in electricity and magnetism, electric currents, conductors and insulators, measuring instruments, electrical laws, electric cells, batteries and accumulators, units of measurement, principles of the dynamo and electric motor and the various electrical circuits employed in the apparatus you will have to use in your aircraft.

You will spend some little time, too, in the laboratories watching demonstrations and doing practical work yourself.

Approximately one-sixth of the course is

occupied in disciplinary instruction, physical training and organised games; and in this connection you will soon realise that smartness in demeanour and action has always been an outstanding feature of the R.A.F. Signals Service.

At the end of the course you will sit for an examination, on the result of which you will be chosen as either a ground operator or a member of an air crew.

The second part of the course is entirely concerned with the practical aspect of the wireless operator/air gunner's duties. You will be given instruction on the signals organisation generally, crew training and aircraft handling, the maintenance of aircraft, W/T equipment, the operation of aircraft sets in the laboratory and in air frames. You will appreciate that all these are very important subjects, as a failure on your part to reach a high standard may, at some future date, jeopardise the safety of your whole crew.

Obviously the most interesting part of this course is when you are called upon to operate under actual conditions. Three methods are employed for this instruction: the " Air frame ", where the operator is enclosed in a cabin exactly like the one he will use in an aircraft; the " flying classroom ", in which a number of operators are taken into the air at the same time and given demonstrations under actual conditions; and, finally, the single-engined aircraft, in which you will be taken up alone in order to gain individual air operating experience.

The final stage of the course is the passing-out examination, which is held during the last week.

When all this is over you will be sent to a Bombing and Gunnery School, and from there to an Operational Training Unit, where you will gain actual W/T operating experience, including D/F instruction under crew conditions.

Air Observer

The air observer occupies a vitally important position in aircraft of the Royal Air Force engaged in operations over the sea, or over territory occupied by the enemy.

The success of every bombing raid, every oversea patrol, every long-range interception, and every reconnaissance depends very largely upon the excellence of the air observer's work.

It is recognised that the air observer is responsible for directing the aircraft to and from its objective, and he may well feel proud that it is upon his judgment that the pilot will safely rely for all matters affecting routes to follow, courses to steer, heights at which to fly, weather to be encountered, or simply the position of the aircraft at any particular time. Any duties that demand a high degree of mental activity and skill are always interesting, and for this reason the air observer has a most fascinating and at the same time a most gratifying job in the air.

If you are selected to be an air observer, you must attain a thorough grasp of the theory and practice of air navigation, a sound working knowledge of meteorology, signals, photography, reconnaissance, bombing and gunnery. From the Initial Training Wing you will be sent to an Air Observer Navigation School, where you will be taught everything you must know about the theory of navigation, photography, reconnaissance and meteorology. Your theoretical instruction will be so timed that you will always be sent into the air to practise what you were taught on the ground with as little delay as conditions allow.

From your very first flight you must take care not to waste valuable time in the air; always you must concentrate on the job in hand and develop initiative whenever the opportunity offers. You will never be sent into the air to do anything that you have not been taught, but if you do not understand your instructions, ask for further explanations *before* going up. You will find that you are put in charge of the navigation of aircraft quite early in your practical flying career, so that you will soon acquire a sense of responsibility and a confidence that is essential for efficiency.

From the Air Observer Navigation School you will be sent to a Bombing and Gunnery School, where you will be trained to aim and drop the bomb-load, and also to assist in the defence of your aircraft against possible attacks by enemy fighters.

The syllabus of bombing training embraces all aspects of the duties of an air observer as a bomb aimer, and includes lectures on theory of bomb sighting and bomb sights, bombs and components, bomb carriers, and bombing practice.

The syllabus of Gunnery training embraces all aspects of the duties of an observer when called upon to man one of the gun positions in defence of his aircraft. This syllabus is similar to that of the air gunner's course.

You will find that air training commences as soon as the necessary initial lectures have been given. You will then have to carry out wind-speed and direction-finding exercises, before going on to such things as bombing exercises with practice bombs against targets moored in the sea.

As with the other courses, quite a lot of time is devoted to physical training and organised games, as physical fitness is a necessity to efficiency in the air.

On satisfactory completion of the course, you will be awarded the air observer's brevet and granted the temporary rank of sergeant.

So far in your training you will have been alongside other air observers on purely training types of aircraft, but now you will be sent to an Operational Training Unit, where you will come into close contact with the pilots, wireless operators and air gunners on the type of aircraft that you will all shortly man together against the enemy. Opportunities will be afforded to establish firmly your growing prowess as an air navigator, but your time will mostly be occupied in learning the refinements that are essential to an air observer required to be not only a reliable navigator, but also a useful member of a highly technical service.

Pilot

There remains the possibility that you will be selected for pilot duties.

Pilots undergo their flying training in three stages :

(1) Elementary Flying Training School (E.F.T.S.).

(2) Service Flying Training School (S.F.T.S.).

(3) Operational Training Unit (O.T.U.).

At the E.F.T.S. you learn to fly on light type aircraft of about 100 horse power. These aircraft are easy to fly, and by the time you leave the School you will find that you can fly quite competently, that you will be able to do a little aerobatics, and that you will have done your first cross-country flight. You will also have gained from your lectures elementary knowledge of Armament, Parachutes, Navigation and Meteorology, Signals and Aircraft and Ship Recognition. You will also have done quite a few hours on the Link Trainer, which is an ingenious device that simulates blind-flying conditions.

At the conclusion of your E.F.T.S. course you will be recommended for either single-engine or twin-engine training at the S.F.T.S. This recommendation will depend on your various abilities and your temperament, but as far as possible your own wishes in this respect will be met. You must appreciate that the qualities called for in a good fighter pilot are quite different from those in a good bomber pilot.

At your S.F.T.S. you will be introduced to powerful advanced training aircraft, aircraft which have all the multifarious devices that are incorporated in the modern operational machine, and your time at the S.F.T.S. will be spent in learning to fly this rather complicated type of aircraft. You will also learn such things as formation flying and low operational flying, and you will carry out quite long cross-country flights of 200–300 miles. You will, too, have gained confidence and experience in instrument flying.

At the end of your course at the S.F.T.S., and provided you pass the necessary ground examination and flying tests, you will be granted your " wings ". And this is the moment, too, that recommendations for commissions are made.

If you are recommended, you will proceed to the Operational Training Unit as a Pilot Officer; if you are not (and not everyone can be), you will go as a Sergeant Pilot.

At the Operational Training Unit you will fly the type of aircraft with which your future squadron is equipped. You will learn how to use your aircraft as a weapon and as a unit in a squadron, and you will be taught the latest tactical lessons that have been derived from contact with the enemy. Then, when you have absorbed all this, you will be posted to an operational squadron.

As the R.A.F. is a continually expanding Force, there is a constant need for more flying instructors. Most of these instructors are drawn from units, but if you show exceptional prowess at your S.F.T.S. you may be recommended to become an instructor.   If this is the case, you will undergo an Instructor's course at that Mecca of flying technique, the Central Flying School.   On completion of this course you will be a fully fledged instructor, and will then be posted back to a Flying Training School to help carry on the good work of turning out more and yet more pilots.

This chapter is introduced by quoting the Prime Minister's stirring reference to the Royal Air Force. His tribute was due to the fulfilment by the Service, to which you may soon belong, of the aim set in its motto.   Keep this motto in the forefront of your mind :

"PER ARDUA AD ASTRA"

NOTES

NOTES

GIVE INSTRUCTION TO A WISE MAN...